PRAISE ...

The Endodontist's 2019 Guide to Creating Personal and Financial Freedom

"I've known Ace for thirty-five years and he has always been focused on value, quality, self-improvement, and mentoring others. This book is a continuation of those attributes and gives the reader the skills and knowledge to live a life of peace, joy, hope, contentment, achievement, and financial freedom. By putting his principles into action, you will be able to claim 'victory,' and that success will spread to your office staff, your patients, and, most importantly, your family."

—JAMES C. KULILD, DDS, MS, past president, American Association of Endodontists; diplomate, American Board of Endodontics; professor emeritus, Department of Endodontics UMKC School of Dentistry

"Every dentist should keep this book bedside and read and re-read it. The advice is sound, easy to understand and implement. I consider Ace Goerig as a combination of John Bogle and Warren Buffett for dentists who want a secure financial future."

—DAN SOLIN, author of the Smartest series of investing books

"Dr. Ace Goerig is a genius when it comes to unlocking the key to happiness in life! He loves sharing his easy-to-implement secrets of contentment, enthusiasm and living the good life . . . all at the same time. For decades he has studied burned-out employers/employees in the workforce. From the CEO/owner to the entry level employees, workers are simply tired of the noose around their necks called DEBT!

"We all know that debt reduction at a fast pace is the key to this thirst for 'working because we love it' versus hating for Monday to roll around to go back to the paycheck-to-paycheck existence.

"Ace's book outlines exactly what others can do to achieve this outrageous happiness in life. There are several key elements: Live below your means early on; pay yourself first each payday; be the most ethical person you know; hire experts to provide the growth in your business that compounds your net by tens of thousands per month. This not only pays down the debt quickly, it allows you to work because you 'get to' rather than 'have to.' That folks, is pure happiness!"

—**LINDA MILES**, founder/CEO Linda Miles & Associates; founder, Speaking Consulting Network

"It's an easy read with a lot of helpful insight into current investment theory as a small business owner. In addition, the references allow the reader to pursue aspects of personal growth, financial freedom, and debt reduction using outside sources vetted by the author.

"My personal experience with Endo Mastery and Ace's guidance have helped me to live life without debt, with ease and flow in the office working three days a week, and with joy, peace, and prosperity in all aspects of my life.

"Read the book and follow the program. It worked for me and it can work for you!"

—**MICHAEL FELDMAN**, DMD; diplomate, ABE New York; twenty-year client and former skeptic

"I have found that the most significant changes in my life turn on very small hinges. My decision to enroll in Ace's Endo Mastery coaching program and to implement the principles taught in this book have made all the difference in my life. The best investment you can make is in your own practice and yourself. Thanks to Ace's great coaching, I have added an additional $1 million in yearly personal production and will be completely debt free in three months. That's a 1400% yearly return on my initial investment into the program for the rest of my professional life! His systems and philosophy have helped me achieve this with less stress and more enjoyment than I have ever experienced in my twenty-year career. I shudder to think of what it would have cost if I had let my pride or fear keep me from being coachable. Thank you, Ace, for making such a difference in mine and my family's life!"

—DAVID WILSON, DDS, endodontist, Oregon

"This book is a great outline on how to live your life with freedom! Freedom financially, freedom to choose a purposeful life, and the freedom to share that life with others. I encourage and challenge the reader to proceed with a 'can-do' attitude. The general knee-jerk reaction to change is negative. What a shame. Life is always changing, so why shouldn't we change with it? We can be happier, more insightful, and motivating to our friends and family to do the same.

"I first met Endo Mastery and Ace in 2001. I employed his coaching program shortly thereafter. The first year of coaching I increased my collections by $300,000! Over the years I have brought the coaching team back into my office. I just completed my fourth year of coaching. I work 3 days a week and average 138 days of work per year. I have less stress and more happiness at work. I tell my patients and friends that this is the greatest hobby in the world. I can't imagine doing anything else. We work with great people, meet new and wonderful people every day and serve our community!"

—WILLIS GABEL, DDS, endodontist, Washington state

"To Ace, your most recent book is wonderful, a distillation of your many experiences in the constant quest for improvement, from the spiritual to office management, investing, and looking inward to find happiness. Happiness, after all, is what we all want. Kendrick was right. 'If you don't enjoy the process, you will not enjoy the destination.' I want to thank you for helping me to enjoy the process. The study club that we were a part of twenty-eight short years ago was one of the best aspects of my professional career. It was a great time of change with the microscopes, rotary instrumentation, MTA, and single-appointment endodontic treatment. The change continues today with the Endo Mastery coaching and resulting staff, marketing and scheduling changes. Thankfully, another wonderful mentor of mine shared the concept of 'spend less than you make.' I love to see you sharing that with others. It has allowed me to be debt free for many years now. We are fortunate to be in this profession. Sometimes we get mired in the difficulty of our practice lives. Thanks to you and Endo Mastery for helping us to improve our circumstance."

—**STEVE MCNICHOLAS**, DDS, MS; diplomate, American Board of Endodontics; California

"When we first met Ace, we were completing around four cases per day. It was a good living, but I was frustrated with being able to recruit appropriate staffing with the associated cash flow. I epitomized the 'cheap' dentist stereotype, trying to save enough to build a retirement account. As a previous aerospace engineer, I knew the process could be optimized as was evident from Dr. Goerig's example of a consistent fourteen completions per day. Through coaching and the study group, we now consistently complete ten treatments per day in a comfortable office flow. The office management techniques helped us to weather the business through a personal bout with cancer.

"Ace doesn't teach endodontics. Residency did that. The coaching and the consequent study group teaches endodontic office process flow and personal growth. It was stress relief so we could concentrate on the endo. The office flow now allows us to provide marvelous bonuses for our employees (this year taking them to Hawaii), and we are securing a retirement that many dream about."

—**WILLIAM S. DODSON, JR.**, DMD, endodontist, Virginia

"This book is a must-have. While it is easy to read and the information is keen, it really works! We were doubtful at first but if we can do it, you can too. Of course, Ace and Endo Mastery have been available and ready to keep us on track with measurable goals and tracking to see trends. Even though we have adopted this philosophy of more ease and grace for over twenty-five years in our endo practice, we are still happy in our practice while we continue to grow our business. The philosophy describes in this powerful, yet simple read continues to assist us to adapt to the changes in clinical care, practice management and all the way through to retirement. Interestingly enough it starts with being debt free. It is a complete package. Find a way through or around whatever blocks you to get on this path of more ease, more joy in practice and in life. Read it, use it and you prosper! I really appreciate the systems and simple brilliance in this book."

—**CLARA STUPARITZ,** practice manager for Advanced Endodontics PC, Gurnee, Illinois; lead coach for Core Team Leadership, LLC

"This is a great book that every dentist should read whether you are a new grad or experienced clinician. It's a blueprint on how to practice more successfully with less stress. Dr. Goerig also presents a well-thought-out investment plan that includes getting out of debt and investing in low-cost passive index funds. (I wish I had heard this investment plan earlier in my career). Finally, Ace shares his philosophy on how to be happy, which includes 'getting rid' of the 'stuff' in our lives that interferes with having a happy, less stressful life. I can't recommend this book enough!"

—**DR. ROBERT KANE,** Goodyear, Arizona, a very satisfied client for over fifteen years

"The content of this book is tremendously valuable and life changing. Based on my own personal experience, it has a potential to impact both one's professional and personal life. I have worked with Endo Mastery for the last fifteen years and attest to the power of these principles. I am so grateful to be a part of something so life changing and truly hope that others can benefit from it as well. My recommendation is to commit to it and be consistent. You will be amazed!"

—**SHAHIN ETEMADI**, endodontist, Washington state

"Here it is in a wonderful, compact nutshell—the 'crux' of the Ace Goerig philosophy of endodontic practice, personal finance, and life boiled down to this beautiful blueprint for happiness in our practice and personal life! Why 'recreate the wheel' when you have the best mentor in our specialty generously sharing his experiences and wisdom to us for a life filled with peace, joy and fulfillment? This book is a must-read for all endodontists and gives us life skills to share with our loved ones, too!"

—**RICHARD C. WITTENAUER**, DDS, diplomate, ABE, California

"I have been a coaching client since . . . opening a solo practice the day after graduating from my residency in 2006, and then hired Ace's team for a tune-up in 2014. I am a member of his Mastery Circle, which allows me to grow professionally each year. His blueprint for success really does work! It has allowed me to become financially free as a relatively young man, and now I have a full-time associate. We both work three days a week, never more than two days in a row, and take plenty of time off. I used to see myself with a target date of retirement in my early fifties. But now that I work less and have no money concerns, I will likely do the profession I love late into life. This new book lays out his blueprint in such a simple and informative way. It's a must-read for any small business owner who wants to work less and make more."

—**PAUL ABBOTT**, DMD, endodontist, Kentucky

"Ace makes financial planning easy and this book provides a great starting point. I started using this very information in 2014 and was in the coaching program in 2016 when I found out I had complications associated with pregnancy. Because I had his systems in place and was already on my way to financial freedom, I was able to fly across the country numerous times for the best possible care without worrying about my corporate or personal finances. I recouped the money I spent on coaching back within about two months; it was one of the best investments I ever made."

—**ALY PHEE**, BSc, DMD, Diplomate ABE, FRCD(C); Saskatchewan, Canada

"In this book, Ace provides the reader with an easy-to-follow program for achieving and living the abundant life. He outlines how to have an abundance of time, money, and inner peace. Following the principles Ace teaches, I'm living a life of financial freedom, predictable prosperity in my practice, and greater happiness. Hiring Ace and his team at Endo Mastery has been an essential key to the success I now enjoy."

—**J. KENDALL SNOW**, DDS, MS, endodontist, North Carolina

"Game changer! I initially was interested in Ace's efficiency within his office. When I heard him lecture and got to know him, I was more astonished by his inner peace and calm demeanor. He has systems that when put in place . . . flat out work. In my first year with Endo Mastery coaching, my collections went up 30%. I was so pleased with the results I did a second year, and we are again on our way to an additional 30% increase in collections. This increase in cash flow has come with less stress, less aggravation, and less days worked! My office is properly staffed to accommodate and manage this increase in flow. I have also practiced Ace's philosophy on debt reduction and it has brought about a sense of control and calmness over my finances and life. I would say that Ace has been one of the most influential people that has had a dramatic and positive effect on my life!

"One of the other great things about Ace is that he truly wants you to succeed. He has written this tell-all book that divulges all his secrets. There is so much useful and specific information that can make your practice really exceed all expectations. It is an extremely quick read that can change your life. He has certainly changed mine."

—**BRIAN T. WYCALL**, DDS, PC, endodontist, Maryland

"As an endodontist in practice for 15 years I have often struggled with who to believe when it came to investing and a financial philosophy for life. I often was torn between what was the best way to live and spend and save. It is such an important topic with so many different opinions on the 'right way'. I found Ace 5 years ago and he and his philosophy have totally changed my life and all the secrets are contained in this short book. I truly believe that this is the 'right' way and have made a commitment to read this book at the beginning of each year to remind myself. Thank you, Ace. I am now living a more meaningful, happy, purposeful, almost debt free life because of you and your relentless passion to help others."

—**DEREK WHITE**, DDS, endodontist, Madison, MS.

"*Dr. Ace's Financial Blueprint* is a life changing plan that I have found to be extremely beneficial. One part of its brilliance is the simplicity of his strategy. This financial objective is just one part of the total makeover that Ace is all about. I have found Ace's program to be all encompassing. He delves into all aspects of the office as well as the personal and financial realms. I have thrown myself into his program wholeheartedly and have found happiness and peace that have eluded me to this point. The investment I have made in Ace's programs has been the best money I have ever spent. Thank you Ace!!!"

—**GERALD J. GRAY**, DDS MS, Endodontist, Minnesota

"Ace Goerig has spent much of his life passionately and intentionally studying all aspects of the endodontic office. I'm incredibly grateful for his generosity in sharing what he has learned. Ace has done an amazing job of putting a lifetime of knowledge, wisdom and valuable experience into this great book. I strongly recommend it to all endodontists that want to have more fun, make more money, work less, and have less stress in their lives. The principles found in this book have helped hundreds of endodontists like me take their practices to a new level. I used Ace's coaching program 15 years ago when I started my practice; with his help, I was able to become very productive and profitable quickly. I am sure that the program paid for itself many times over in just the first year of being in practice. The financial freedom that I have been able to achieve has allowed me to have less stress, spend more time with my family and serve others. What a blessing! Thank you Ace for your excellent guidance and mentorship. There is no better book out there on how to be a successful endodontist. I highly recommend this book!"

—**CHRISTOPHER D SMITH**, DDS, endodontist, Arizona

*The Endodontists 2019 Guide to Creating
Personal and Financial Freedom*
by Dr. Albert (Ace) Goerig

© Copyright 2019 Dr. Albert (Ace) Goerig

ISBN 978-1-63393-797-0

Published by

ENDO MASTERY

222 Lilly Rd. NE
Olympia, WA 98506
endomastery.com

THE ENDODONTIST'S 2019 GUIDE

TO CREATING PERSONAL AND FINANCIAL FREEDOM

DR. ALBERT "ACE" GOERIG

Contents

Preface

AS ENDODONTIST WE HAVE one of the greatest professions and as Americans, we live in one of the greatest countries in the world with all the opportunities to have a life of our dreams. Yet many endodontist have yet to find happiness and contentment in their practice and their lives. One problem is that we were not taught in dental school the secrets of creating a great, fun and profitable practice. Nor do we have enough education or understanding about personal finance and investing. We think we will get rich through investing, but many endodontist lose money by placing it into several various so-called investments that they know nothing about, such as unnecessary whole life insurance policies, risky stocks and speculative real estate, hedge funds, commodities, day trading, and limited partnerships, hoping they will strike it rich. We forget that the real money is made in our practice, and the best investment we can make is to pay off our debts first before we invest anywhere. Paying off debt is investing and gives you the maximum guaranteed return without any risk. We need to learn to love what we do and focus on creating a practice that is fun and profitable. My mentor, Kendrick Mercer, taught me that "Life is a process, not an end; if you don't enjoy the process, you'll hate the end!" This book is about learning to enjoy the process.

Through a simple and specific guide, you will be able to increase your practice profitability, pay off debts quickly and reach financial freedom while you savor and enjoy every precious moment of your life to the fullest. In this book, I will show you the most efficient way to become financially free by using the two vehicles that can get you an over 100% return on your money, guaranteed. Using this approach, most doctors could be debt-free in three to five years and financially free in ten years. You will learn how to enjoy work more while creating an incredible relationship with your patients, team and family. The rewards are many. But most of all, I urge you to enjoy the process.

Dr. Albert C. (Ace) Goerig
Olympia, Washington
July, 2019

Foreward

I GREW UP IN RURAL PENNSYLVANIA in what most would consider a lower-income family. When I was in high school my father transferred to California for a job, which introduced me to a very different social lifestyle. Unlike my rural upbringing, California brought with it an amazing sense of fast-pace America unlike anything I had previously experienced.

As a youth, I was imprinted with the sense that I should become "better" than my parents, and I strived to be just that. I dealt with my own insecurities and felt alone many times as I grew into what is now "me."

Fast-forwarding to my endodontic residency at the University of Texas Health Science Center in Houston, Dr. Goerig visited our facility and focused particular attention on the residents. When our day of sharing ended, I was very adamant that I wanted to share his philosophical viewpoint in terms of life and practice. I learned then that our practice of endodontics could be the fuel for our life and lifestyle, and I wanted to maximize that possibility.

After that one-time meeting, I never expected I would rub elbows with such a visionary in endodontics and in life again, yet I held the virtues of possibility within me. I was simple in those days, expecting little, wishing for more.

In 1997, I received a mailer at my office announcing that Dr. Goerig was presenting a two-day seminar on practice management in San Francisco. I instantly knew I needed to attend. At the time, I was a year and a half out of residency and had just opened my own endodontic private practice. I attended the course and was again dazzled with the possibilities he shared. I wanted to learn more, and in private discussion he invited me to join his newly started coaching program. This was a no-brainer for me, as the philosophy—not the promises—were highly attractive.

I was coached for one year with Dr. Goerig's company and have never looked back. His teachings, which are well represented in this book, were life-changing. I exponentially increased my practice to a level I thought unimaginable for this small-town boy.

I continued my journey without coaching for years, always remembering and employing the virtues of Dr. Goerig's teachings. Dr. Goerig and I remained close friends and colleagues during these many years, and he introduced me to many additional mentors, including Kendrick Mercer, who you will meet in this book.

Later in practice, following some ups and downs, I reconnected with Dr. Goerig's Endo Mastery team once again. I have been working with their coaching for four years running now and am so grateful for his and his team's support, and for the results!

Dr. Goerig's philosophy is about more than just ramping up your practice and increasing your income. It is the entire package. He shares a philosophy about life, relationships, deserve levels, abilities, joy, less stress, and pure appreciation, satisfaction and peace with where everyone is at any given moment. For me, my philosophy is no longer based on a measuring stick but rather on my appreciation for who I am, my abilities, and what I want to accomplish in life. And, as a reminder, the fuel for my life and lifestyle is my practice.

Dr. Goerig will enlighten you as to how your endodontic practice and your life stories intertwine and feed upon one another. You will learn how enjoying your practice in the now will create a sense of wellness and peace and fuel not only your retirement and lifestyle, but also magnificent relationships with others, including your supporting team members.

Every individual and every endodontist are unique. From personal experience, I know that Dr. Goerig's insight and philosophy can be tailored to each person. Earlier, I spoke of my successes. Allow me to share more of my story.

As I drifted from the coaching of Dr. Goerig in the early 2000s, life swallowed me up in financial and relationship debt and left me in a dark place. In fact, you might say that I was living the American dream! With Dr. Goerig's principles, I reshaped my mindset and was able to shed more than a million dollars of debt and heaviness in less than four years. I became completely debt free, and through his investing principles I am growing a retirement income that compounds exponentially every day—something I never could have dreamed of.

I closely follow his coaching advice and have trimmed my work week to three days, earn the same handsome income (alongside a wonderful associate doctor), and am living more fully than ever. In my experience, abundance followed the process of becoming debt free, and this phenomenon unleashed amazing practice growth, profitability and ease in my life and lifestyle—exactly what Dr. Goerig teaches. Although I foresee being financially able to soon retire, I am now at a place where working is fun and no longer a drain, and I expect to work (perhaps less and less) and "retire in practice" as the "Ace Process" describes.

My family encoded me to expect little and to "earn my keep." Dr. Goerig enabled me to visualize the possibilities of every facet of my life, especially my practice, which in turn has propelled me to reach my greater potential. Remember that even the greatest athletes and Olympians use coaches to assist them in excelling. I often wonder why someone would not "hitch their wagon to a star" and learn from those who excel and who genuinely want to share and cheerlead your success! Mentors of this mindset are few and far between. I invite you to peruse

Dr. Goerig's philosophy, and I ask that you be open to the possibilities of how his philosophy can be tailored to your personal dreams and vision.

With the greatest admiration and appreciation,

Brian Hornberger,
DDS, MS, endodontist

Chapter 1:

CREATE AN INCREDIBLE LIFE STORY

IN A MAY 2017 INTERVIEW with Charlie Rose, Warren Buffett was asked what gave him his greatest joy. *"I love going to the office,"* said Buffett. *"It has been my painting for over fifty years: I get to paint what I want, and I own the brush and I own the canvas and the canvas is unlimited. And that is a pretty nice game, and I get to do it every day with people I like. I don't have to associate with anyone that causes my stomach to turn. If I were in politics, I'd have to smile at a lot of people I want to hit. I've got a really good deal and I am hanging onto it."*

Most dentist-owners forget that they have the brush and the canvas, and they can create their story any way they want. Sometimes it takes the insight of a coach to help them through the process.

* * *

CREATING YOUR NEW LIFE STORY

We are on this planet for a relatively brief period, and all we have is from now until the end of our lives. So, how can we make the most of this time?

To live our lives to the fullest, we need to create a new vision or story of what is possible. We all can live the rest of our lives as a very exciting adventure. For most of us, because of our cultural context and the lack of training we have received regarding financial matters, it is difficult to set up a guide for reaching financial freedom, or even to recognize that our way of relating to money could be very different. However, if we write a story about how we want to live, it is easy to develop and follow a guide to fulfill that story. But most of us don't know how to develop a coherent and compelling story about financial and personal freedom.

I was raised poor by a single mom. I had a 2.3 GPA in high school and was only accepted into college because I set the state pole-vaulting record. I spent three years studying Engineering, and the Army ROTC taught me how to fly fixed-wing aircraft so I could fly helicopters in Vietnam in 1966. Instead, in 1965, I met my cousin who was a dentist, and he recommended that I go to dental school.

I changed majors and graduated from dental school six years later. I then spent twenty years in the Army as a Dental Corps officer. During that time, my family and I moved twelve times, had many different assignments, and really saw the world from a unique perspective. Life became an incredible story for me. The fun is in always developing new stories, so after I retired from the Army, I began a new story, and after a difficult start I created a very successful dental practice. Eventually I developed a dental consulting company to share my story with other endodontist who were struggling, just as I had, so I could help them create a beautiful story for *their own practice and lives.*

The best stories are specific and flexible—specific in offering a full vision with rich detail, and flexible because life is a process and we are always growing. As new experiences arise, we begin to see things at a deeper level. When situations change, we need to give ourselves permission to change our minds to stay within our own integrity. You can create a beautiful story that incorporates abundance into your life. Having your finances in order will help support your positive story so you can live life fully. However, writing a life story takes great courage, because it involves change. Sometimes you need to change many things to live a free and independent life. In this case, you are called upon to face your fears of confrontation and conflict and to create the life you want. Your story shows the world your intent to change and starts you on your new path. Gandhi was once asked, "What is your message to the world?" He replied, "My life is my message." What is your message to your children?

How to Bring Abundance in Your Life

The reason we create positive stories is to let the universe know what we want. I personally believe that we can bring anything—positive or negative—into our lives depending on our thoughts. This happens by creating a clear, positive vision of exactly what we want and know (believe) that it will come about. This could be an increase in referrals, doing more cases, finding the right associate or team member. Over 100 years ago, in his book, "The Science of Getting Rich," Wallace Wattles talked about focusing on what you want and not what you don't want in your life. We need to put our energies into the creative and not the competitive aspects of life. I never spend any time worrying about what the other dentist is doing. Why? Because there is unlimited abundance, and if we have the right focus and vision, we can bring whatever we want into our lives. The real fun is helping others create abundance in their lives. I spend little time listening to the negative events in the news which I cannot control. The real joy and happiness comes from relationships with family and in my practice. Abundance always comes when we are thankful for all the gifts and richness that we have in our life.

My Ninety-Year-Old Millennial Story: Retire in Practice

As members of the Baby Boomer generation, most of us were taught to work hard, put in the hours, take three weeks' vacation a year, and retire after forty years of practice to play golf and enjoy the sunsets. Yet many dentists still work after age sixty-five not because they want to, but because they have to, due to poor management of money, or because they have had too many "successful" marriages.

We look down upon the millennials because they seem to be more interested in enjoying life now, taking more time for themselves and their families, and are not as concerned with money as we Baby Boomers were. Yet down deep, those two generations are more alike than not. Because of our cultural imprinting, we did not know that we could write a better story. Both generations see the possibility. Let me tell you about my ninety-year-old millennial.

When I first came to Olympia, Washington as an endodontist in 1991, one of my favorite referring dentists came in for a root canal. He was in his seventies yet looked like he was in his forties. I commented on how great he looked, and I asked him what his secret was. He told me that he had "retired in practice" only ten years out of dental school.

In the 1950s, when he had graduated, most dentists worked five days a week and took about two weeks' vacation a year. After a year in practice, his classmate told him that he could really work four days a week if he just modified his schedule, and he could make just as much money and have more time off. He did, and it worked. He told me he and his wife were not big spenders, so they were able to pay off the mortgage on their house and on the practice debt within ten years of graduation.

After that, he realized that he only needed to work three days a week. He started taking more vacations each year to be with his family, enjoy his hobbies, take continuing education courses, and to relax and be much more creative in the way he ran the practice. He paid his team on salary, so they also had time off. He eventually retired at age eighty-two and enjoyed his very long and loving marriage. He came by my office in his early nineties and showed me pictures of himself skiing on the top of Mount Rainier with his great-grandson, and fly-fishing with his daughter. He recently passed away, shortly after his wife died. I am sure he enjoyed his millennial-style life.

What most of us do not realize is that we, too, can enjoy this retire-in-practice story (more specifics on how to retire in practice in Part Five). We just need to create it, and in dentistry we can. We can do this by getting out of debt as soon as possible, and by creating a practice that we love that is profitable and fun. Benjamin Franklin retired from business at age 46 to have more time to work on other interest and to contribute to the well-being of society while creating a personal legacy. What will be your legacy?

Don't do stupid things with money. The main mistake endodontist make is living beyond their means right out of school and burying themselves in debt. Instead, know that you will have plenty of money to get out of debt quickly. Once you are debt-free, learn to invest consistently and safely on your own in a secure environment and you will never worry about money again. With the right guide this is all possible, and that is what I will show you in this book.

The Great American Scam consists of monthly debt payments and has changed the American Dream into a nightmare. We are lulled into a false sense of security and ownership. The banks have trained (fooled) us to stay in debt our whole lives through credit cards, mortgages, refinancing and other loans, while they take from us two-thirds of our life's earnings in monthly debt payments. Unfortunately, most endodontist do not understand how our money system really works.

A Tale of Two Endodontists

Let's compare the tales of two twenty-eight-year-old endodontists.

Endodontist A earns $250,000 a year. He has fallen for the scam and lives big. He buys the big practice, big home, expensive cars, and other toys to build ego and find happiness while continually creating debt and making monthly payments. He has no money for practice consultants.

After thirty years, he has paid off his mortgage, practice, and school loan, but at age fifty-eight, he still has a second mortgage, car payments, credit cards, timeshare payments and other debts, and only $225,000 in savings.

He resents going in to work because he is working to pay off debt and not for the relationships or the fun of it. This creates poor relationships with his family, patients, and team.

He will give to his creditors two-thirds of his life's earnings, including the taxes he has paid on that income. And along with that, he will have given up his freedom and a life of choice which will keep him working for many more years because he *has* to—not because he *wants* to.

Endodontist B also earns $250,000 a year. However, Endodontist B lives simply, like a student, and she learns how to be profitable in dentistry, allowing her to pay off all debts, including credit cards, car, mortgage, school loans, and practice debt in ten years. She brings in a practice management consultant, Endo Mastery, who helps her increase her net profit to $600,000 a year. Endo mastery helps her bring in an associate so that she can work only three days a week. She eventually increases her net income to $1 million per year. This allows her to put in $30,000 a month into her Personal Bank earning 4% to 6% tax-free. This will be described in Chapter 8.

At age thirty-eight, she has no debt, has retired in practice, and now works because she *wants* to, not because she *has* to. She loves going in to the office three days a week with eight to twelve weeks off a year for vacation to be with her family and friends. She now has 60% to 70% of this income to invest for retirement, children's education, travel, or charitable contributions.

Having an associate allows the office to be open five days a week. Even though she only works 120 days a year, she will earn much more than, Endodontist A does, except she will go to the office for the relationships and the fun, not because she needs the money. She now has the time to expand her relationships, enjoy other pursuits, and even make a difference in her community and the world. At age fifty-eight, she will have been debt free for twenty years and, because of her increase in net profit, she will have over $12 million in her tax-free personal bank and $27 million in her life insurance death benefit.

You Can Become a Millionaire

Here are the lessons from the book, *The Millionaire Next Door*, by Thomas Stanley and William Danko. Wealth is not the same as your income. Wealth is what you accumulate (net worth) and not what you spend. Wealth comes from hard work, dedication, planning and self-discipline. Millionaires do not live in upscale neighborhoods or drive fancy cars. A millionaire's goal is to become financially independent which is much more important than displaying high social status. These financially successful people control their consumption and do not allocate too much money to products and services. Millionaires are frugal and not only live below their means, they live *well* below their means. Most millionaires live in an average home, drive a used car and their children go to public schools. They are married to the same spouse who is also a conservative spender. Warren Buffett, one of the richest men in the world, has lived in the same modest house for more than sixty years, sent his children to public schools and drives an eight-year-old car.

We all have choices on where we want to spend our money. We could buy a smaller house, go on fewer vacations, buy a smaller car or put more money in investments. Most people do not consciously sit down and consider their choices but instead they haphazardly spend their money without focus. Until we are debt-free, we are restrained by our income, so we need to create a game plan and focus our excess money to draw a guide to personal and financial success.

Writing Your Own Story

Most endodontist I work with want to have more time off to enjoy their family, hobbies and personal time. Many of them are burdened by long-term debt, are stressed at work and exhausted when they come home. They are unable to see the possibilities that life and their profession have to offer. Before we create the life we want, we must first imagine it. With the right vision and game plan, they could be debt-free within two to seven years, work three or four days a week in a drama-free, stress-free office with the people they like. Once debt-free, they could take six to ten weeks' vacation a year and have plenty of time to be with and create incredible relationships with family. So, whether you are a practice owner or an associate, you have the canvas and you have the brush to create the life of your dreams. This book was created for you, to show you the possibilities in your practice and personal life and give you the tools and ideas to create your story. As you go through the book, write down the things you want to change in your life, and the steps that you will take to create your new life story. The possibilities are endless.

Chapter 2:

THE FASTEST WAY TO BECOME FINANCIALLY FREE

WHEN PUTTING ALL INVESTMENTS IN PERSPECTIVE, the best returns are from paying off debt and increasing your practice profitability. These choices can give you a return of over 100%. Below are the past ten years' average returns on various investments.

- **Home:** 0-5%. According to Zillow, while home prices have appreciated nationally at an average annual rate between 3% and 5%, depending on the index used for the calculation, home value appreciation in different metro areas can appreciate at markedly different rates than the national average. Over time, home values grew about 0% after inflation. Plan on spending 5% of the value of the home to buy it, 10% to sell it, and 1% to 2% a year to maintain it.
- **Average actively managed fund investment:** 2.6%. According to *Forbes* ("Why The Average Investor's Investment Return Is So Low," Sean Hanlon, Apr 24, 2014), the average investor in a blend of equities and fixed-income mutual funds has earned only a 2.6% or less net annualized rate of return for the ten-year period.
- **Inflation:** The current inflation rate reported by the US Department of Labor for the United States is 2.8% for the twelve months that ended May 2018. Remember that a 3% inflation reduces your 10%

stock return to only 7%. But it also can reduce your 2% return on bonds to a negative 1%.

- **Short Term Bonds:** Over the past five years, bonds have returned only 1.4% annually.
- **Personal Bank (infinite banking concept):** Over the past 30 years it has provided a **guaranteed tax-free** return of 4% to 5% (see chapter 8 and go to personalbank4u.com).
- **S&P 500:** The most recent annual 15-year return on this index is 8.8%, although the average over the past 50 years has been around 7%.
- **No fee investing:** Paying no fees on your investments results in getting you up to 70% more on your investments. Paying 1% to 4% in fees to financial advisors, brokers or mutual fund companies that actively manage your investments could cost you 70% of your return, making you work ten to fifteen years longer before you can retire. If you pay fees of 3% and your investments return only 4%, you got 25% of the return and your broker and mutual fund got 75% of the return. What happens when the return is only 2%? Your commissioned broker's mantra is "heads I win, tails you lose." Learn to invest on your own. This book will show you how.
- **Routine practice fee increases:** Can produce a 10% to 30% increase in net profit.
- **Paying off debt:** Up to 1,000% (10x) return.
- **Dental practice management consulting:** Up to 1,000% (10x) increase on return of investment over time.

Most of your advisors will not appreciate these numbers because each of them looks through a different lens based on their experience and training, and each of them will have a different agenda for you and your money. Your banker's motivation is to get your money into their bank, so they can loan it back to you. Your CPA gets paid to do your state and federal income tax and keep you out of tax difficulty. Because most accountants do not understand business and are risk-averse, their advice would be not to do coaching because they cannot understand the benefits and they see it as just an expense. Surprisingly, some CPAs are concerned that an increase in your net income would increase your taxes and that would be a bad thing. Your investment advisor will encourage you to put your money into your investments and a 401(k) plan, so they can continue to receive fees. When it comes to your money, you are the only one who cares more about it than any of your advisors.

You will see how the power of paying off debt can give you a guaranteed return of 100% to over 1,000%, without risk or tax consequence. Many owner/endodontist could significantly improve their net profit 100% in one year by bringing in a competent consultant. This is magnified to over 1,000% in ten years.

Everyone needs to focus on what investment of your time and money produces the greatest returns. If you execute the last four strategies correctly, then you will have more money than you will ever need, which you can trade in for time, freedom and choices. The market becomes a place to compound some of your excess money. I will show you the best strategies to safely get the best returns by yourself, without paying the extraordinarily high fees and commissions of financial advisors and brokers.

Once debt-free, a dentist would be able to maintain their lifestyle, fund their retirement and only need to work three days a week, and still take off eight to twelve weeks a year, which I call *retire-in-practice*. They could create a beautiful story and environment for themselves and their teams, and love going to the office knowing that they have plenty of time off to play. Under those circumstances, why would you ever want to retire?

When this strategy is implemented correctly, you will have created an automatic investment program through index funds and you will not worry about the ups and downs of the market. Knowing that you are in for the long run and will not sell, eventually you can live off all the dividends of these funds. Remember that increasing the productivity of your practice and paying off all debt first, before investing in the market, will safely provide the highest returns with much more predictability.

* * *

FREEDOM FACTS

The fastest way to become financially free is to pay off all debts before you put money anywhere else. **The advantages to paying off debt first are:**

1. Easiest and simplest to do and understand.
2. Can make over 100% return on your money, guaranteed, without risk or tax consequence.
3. Can be done automatically, right out of your bank account.
4. Changes you from a spender into a saver.
5. You can now invest more into higher return stocks like the S&P 500 index fund because your paid-off home acts like a long-term inflation-adjusted bond. The 20% of your income that you were using to pay off your mortgage now becomes a bond-like investment getting 20% return on your paid-off home.
6. Once debt-free, you have three times the amount of disposable income (previously, two- thirds of your disposable income was paid toward debt) to spend on investments and enjoying life.

One of the biggest misconceptions that keeps you in debt that is perpetuated by banks and accountants is that you should not pay off your house early because when you have a mortgage, you can write off the interest rate on your taxes. This allows the banks to continue to get a large amount of interest from you using your money. If you are in the 28% federal income tax bracket, itemize your deductions and you pay one dollar of mortgage interest and save $.28 in taxes. This means you lose $.72 of the one dollar to save $.28 taxes.

Let's look at this closely: in 2018 an average American couple who pays $10,000 a year in interest on their home loan has the choice of either taking the standard deduction of $24,000 or itemizing their return and taking the $10,000 tax write-off. When they itemize, they are unable to take the standard deduction of $24,000 and have an overall loss of $14,000 in standard deduction. The biggest loss is in the interest you pay the bank, which could range well over 200%.

Please consider a $310,000 mortgage at 4.5% for thirty years. Below, you can see that of the first year's loan payment of $18,849, only $5,001 goes to principal, but $13,848 goes to interest, which is lost forever to you. See Figure 1 below. **This is a 277% loan, not a 4.5% loan.**

In the 28% tax bracket, you had to earn around $17,724 and pay taxes on that to get the $13,847 to give to the bank as interest payments, which makes it a 354% loan. If you had paid an additional principal payment of $5,230.75, you would have eliminated one year's payment and saved $13,617.95 in interest and made 354% return on your money, guaranteed, without risk or any tax consequence.

Year	Interest	Principal	Balance
2019	$13,848	$5,001	$304,999
2020	$13,618	$5,231	$299,768
2021	$13,378	$5,471	$294,297
2022	$13,126	$5,722	$288,575
2023	$12,863	$5,985	$282,590
Total (after 5 years)	$68,833	$27,410	$282,590

FIGURE 1

The reality: over the next five years, you would have paid $96,243 in loan payments and only $27,410 would have gone to pay off the loan. You must understand that the interest is always the highest at the beginning of the loan, and for the first ten years of a 30-year loan the interest paid will always be more than 100%. Always take advantage of this guaranteed high return. **The bottom line: you invested $5,001 and made $13,848, which is a guaranteed 277% return without risk. With this great return, why would anyone not use the money in their savings (only earning less than 1%) to pay off their home? You should also cash out any non-tax-deferred stocks and pay off debts.** Remember, focus on paying off debt before you put your money anywhere else. Once you are debt-free, I will show you specific investment strategies that provide safe and predictable results. Most people can be debt-free within five to ten years using this guide.

Debt Is the Devil

It's all about net worth. Our net worth is the total of all our assets, including our investments, bank accounts and real estate, minus our debts. Paying off debt increases your net worth (wealth) and provides an asset that you can use in emergencies as loan collateral. Paying off debt is a conservative investment strategy. So don't be happy about having more tax deductions, especially when you can't write them off due to the high standard deduction. This is how the government and the banks keep you in debt and in servitude.

There is no good debt; only bad debt. All debt is bad, bad, bad! Debt keeps you imprisoned and prevents you from living a life of freedom, independence and choice. Being overburdened with financial responsibilities increases your stress and can damage important and satisfying personal relationships and even lead to divorce which could cost half of what you own. By changing your spending and saving habits one step at a time, you can regain control of your life. You now know what interest payments really cost you and what to do to change your spending habits.

In John Cummuta's excellent audiobook and manual, *Transforming Debt into Wealth*, he states, "Every time you make a purchase on credit, you need to consider not just the price you're paying for the product, but the price plus interest plus how much that money could have earned you as an investment."

US households now owe $13.15 trillion in total debt, and about $931 billion of that is credit card debt, according to NerdWallet's 2017 American Household Credit Card Debt Study, along with its newly issued quarterly figures. In 2017, the average family's collective balance on all credit cards was more than $16,000. If the family makes just the minimum payment, it would take them thirty-seven and half years to pay off the balance; over that time, they would make total payments of more than $43,000, of which $26,000 would be interest. This is just as if someone said to you, "I will lend you $16,000, and you will pay me back $43,000." If you were to invest the same $26,000 in an individual retirement account (IRA), it would grow to $284,329 over 30 years at 8% interest. We have spent tomorrow's money already and are making payments on it.

With each debt, the interest you pay puts you on the wrong side of the compound interest equation. It's important to realize that you are going to make a finite amount of money in your life. If you give too much of it away in interest payments and impulse buying, there will not be enough money left over for you to retire comfortably. You can take two basic approaches with your money: you can spend it on things that don't add meaning to your life and stay in debt and eat cat food in your retirement years, or you can build your financial future now by paying off debt early and retire early in style. Every dollar you consume now brings you one dollar of value, but every dollar you invest for your future can bring you five to twenty times that amount in your retirement years, allowing you to retire ten to twenty years earlier. Reducing spending and paying off debt will eliminate your money problems and improve your relationships. It will also improve your health by reducing stress. And it will serve as a shining example for your children about what is possible.

How would it feel to be out of debt and to own your home free and clear, with utilities, taxes, and food as your only real expenses? This is possible for everyone if they're following a clear guide. Most people can pay off their credit card debt in one year and their car in the second year. By the third year, they're making extra payments toward their mortgage. Most doctors can be totally debt-free within five to ten years and thereby eliminate payments on student loans, home loans and practice debts.

When you become debt-free, there is no need to worry about your credit report because you pay cash for all your purchases. *The ability to obtain credit is what got you into trouble in the first place.* The idea that you need to build up your credit by borrowing is an illusion that keeps you in debt. But once you become debt-free, no one owns you and this is true freedom.

How to Make 1,000% Interest

Interest rates for dental school loans can average anywhere from 6% to 8% per year. Look at an actual 30-year, $300,000 dental school loan with an interest rate of 7.9% for which the doctor pays $2,180 per month. During the first year of repayment, only $2,556 goes to principal and $23,608 goes to interest. The doctor must earn around $30,000 and pay tax on those earnings, to cover that amount of interest each year. This is more than 1,000% interest. **When determining how much student loan you will need, remember that for every $1,000 you borrow, initially you will have to pay $10,000 back to the bank which does nothing to pay back the loan.**

Year	Interest	Principal	Balance
2019	$23,609	$2,556	$297,444
2020	$23,399	$2,766	$294,678
2021	$23,173	$2,992	$291,686
2022	$22,928	$3,237	$288,449

| 2023 | $22,662 | $3,503 | $284,946 |
| Total (after 5 years) | $115,771 | $15,054 | $284,946 |

FIGURE 2

In this example, by paying another principal payment of $2,765.65 per month, you will eliminate (save) $23,399.34 that you will never have to earn and give the bank, allowing you to make over 1,000% return on your money. This is a no-brainer. Where else can you get 1,000% return on your money guaranteed, without risk? All those endodontist who have student loans must focus on paying off this debt quickly— especially those who are paying high interest rates. If you paid an additional $3,888 per month, your payment would be $6,068 and you would pay the loan off in five years, thus saving $420,835, or about $550,000 before taxes. This is the best deal ever. **The reality:** If you decided not to pay off the loan in five years, then during that five years you would pay $130,825 in payments and only $15,054 would go to pay off the original loan amount.

Steps to Get Rid of Your Dental School Loans Rapidly

1. Just because they will give you a student loan, it does not mean you must take all of it. Remember, for every dollar you borrow you will initially have to pay back ten. Get a part-time job instead and borrow as little as you can handle.
2. Refinance your loan at a lower interest rate as soon as it becomes possible. Go to https://www.whitecoatinvestor.com/12-things-to-know-about-student-loan-refinancing/
3. Live like a student until all your school loans are paid off. If you do not live like a student until your debt is paid off, you will most likely be living like a student when you are retired. This is the most important thing you can do in your career. Work as an associate for

a few years. Take advantage of minority and veteran loans. Commit to paying your school loans off in five years. You and your spouse should create a game plan of getting out of debt which will give you freedom and choices and you can enjoy your relationship. Until you are debt-free, don't worry about getting expensive cars and homes that cause so much financial stress in relationships. Get a coach to show you how to increase your practice's net profit. Learn the secrets to greater efficiency and profitability in the next chapter.

Steps to Eliminate Debt for the Doctor and Team

Eliminating debt is a crucial first step in my guide. The only debt that is reasonable to incur is for the purchase of very large items such as your house, your education, your practice, or your car. Never go into debt for anything else, especially not for consumable items such as vacations.

I can't state it any more clearly: consumption debt is bad, bad, bad, and bad. The best guide is to spend less than you make and to save a substantial amount of your money. Then you can consume with saved dollars. Most families in America are imprinted to use their credit cards and consume, whether they have the money to pay for something or not. When you do this, you typically pay high interest rates; this is not an effective way to manage your money. Instead of a credit card, use a debit card. This way, you pay as you go and you eliminate interest payments. For a step-by-step approach to eliminating debt quickly, see Appendix B, Step-By-Step debt reduction plan.

* * *

CREATING A DEBT-FREE OFFICE

Early in my private practice career, I had a 401(k) plan and even a defined benefit plan. Because the plan was managed by financial advisors and brokers who invested into actively managed funds, the returns were dismal compared to the S&P 500 index fund. Most of my returns went to pay fees to my advisor and the mutual fund company. I also noticed that when people left my practice, they would immediately cash in their retirement plan and spend it on something stupid. If America's Best 401(k) plan had been available at that time, I would have moved my entire plan into that plan and maintained a retirement plan. But because the returns were so poor with my old plans, I decided to eliminate the retirement plans completely, and give each team member a $250 per month debt-reduction bonus. Even now, each year around the Christmas bonus time I have a dinner meeting with my entire team and their spouses, and show them how quickly they can be debt-free using the snowball approach as described in Appendix B. For other doctors who want to help their team get out of debt, I have included the entire audio and video program on my website: DoctorAce.com.

This has been in effect for more than six years, and I have four team members now completely debt-free, and most of my team are now paying off their homes. I have faith that they will be completely debt-free within six to ten years.

But my greatest gift to them is not being out of debt; my greatest gift is that I changed them from spenders into savers. This has done much to eliminate the money issues that many families argue about. Ironically, the only drawback to this plan is that three out of my four team members who are now out of debt do not need to work as much now, and they either work part-time in the practice, or they've left the practice enjoy their hobbies, which can be profitable. But I just bring more people in and get them out of debt. Here is an example of one of those team members.

Lisa's Story

Lisa was my chief clinical dental assistant and was incredibly good at her job. And she had a hobby selling things on eBay. Surprisingly, she was making over $50,000 a year in her hobby.

Her husband was making about $15 an hour on his physically demanding construction job; they decided to live on his income and focus everything she earned from their eBay business, plus her salary from my dental office, toward debt reduction and paying off their two houses. Within four years, they had paid off one mortgage and sold the other home and invested the profits into her company. Once debt free, they can open their own personal bank and put in $20,000 per year and at age 65 will have $700,000 in cash value in their policy and $1,400,000 in death benefit. They can also use the cash value for their business and life purchases.

Lisa has since left my dental practice. She and her husband work about fifteen to twenty hours a week on their eBay business, and have plenty of time for travel and enjoying the adventures of life. They had their first child in November. It is surprising how, with strong intent, becoming debt-free happens very quickly.

Here is How to Eliminate All Your Debt in Three to Five Years

Here is how to quickly pay off all your debt. The average American endodontist takes home around $250,000 a year. Most doctors live on $200,000 which give them $50,000 per year to pay off debt. But in the following chapters I will describe how to become more profitable by using Endo Mastery to increase your income by $520,000 a year with just two additional root canals per day. If your molar root canal fee is $1,300, then two root canals are $2,600. If you did two more cases a day and you worked 200 days a year, then 200 days times $2,600 that is an additional $520,000 each year. Except for some extra gutta-percha, there is no additional overhead associated with these extra two root canals. After paying 35% taxes on the $520,000, you will have an extra $338,000 each year to pay toward debt. You add that to $50,000 of disposable income and you will have $388,000 to pay off debt. Within two years and three months, all your debts will be paid off.

This is the power of doing more treatment cases a day. This is $32,333 extra each month to pay off debt. Once you are debt free, you have that additional $32,333 plus your monthly payments of $10,127, equaling $42,460 per month ($509,524 per year) extra that you will have available for investing and lifestyle. If this was invested in an S&P

500 fund returning 9% annually, you could have $28,613,625 in twenty years. This is called freedom.

$42,460 (2 more root canals per day) paid toward debt principal each month.

Name of Debt	Total Balance (smallest to largest)	Monthly Payment	Accelerated Monthly Payment	Months to pay off
Visa card	$1,000	$30	$42,460	0
Master-Card	$1,500	$32		0
Car 1 at 6% / 3 year	$14,200	$425		0
Car 2 at 6% / 3 year	$21,300	$640	$43,420	1
Dental school at 6% / 30 year	$300,000	$1,800	$45,220	7
Mortgage at 4.5% / 30 year	$400,000	$2,000	$47,220	9
Practice at 4.5% / 10 year	$500,000	$5,200	$52,520	10
Totals	$1,238,000	$10,127 ($121,524/yr.)		27 months (2 yrs/3mo.)

FIGURE 3

Chapter 3:

BECOMING MORE PROFITABLE IN YOUR PRACTICE

YOUR PRACTICE IS YOUR ENGINE, so optimize it to the fullest. You can make more money in your practice by creating efficient systems, providing top-notch customer service, plus a loving and incredible team, high efficiency, and beautiful clinical results.

In 1991, I retired from the US Army after serving twenty years, including twelve moves and multiple job duties from general dentist, endodontist, endodontic resident mentor, and clinic chief, to commanding officer of a dental command. I was from the state of Washington, so when I retired, I just drove south from Seattle until I ran out of traffic and found the beautiful town of Olympia, which needed an endodontist.

A little afraid of opening my practice, I started in a small, three-operatory, 600-square-foot office that another dentist had just left. At that time, I knew very little about opening a practice and had no practice management ideas, so I brought in a local dental consultant to help me set up my systems. She was very helpful, and we implemented systems and hired three assistants and one office administrator.

Being one of only three endodontists for a population area of 200,000, I was swamped with patients and I was working five days a week, ten- to twelve-hour days, killing myself and my team. What I did not understand was how to schedule patients properly to result in very low production.

After the first year, I was exhausted and wondered if I should have just retired from dentistry completely. There was a lot of complaining and drama from my overworked team. Some days I would drive up to the office and think that I should maybe just keep on driving. One Sunday, I came into the office and was going through the front desk drawers and noticed a lot of bills that had not been paid, and checks that had not been deposited. It turned out that the woman up front was overwhelmed with her duties but had not told me.

Eventually, I realized that I was nine months behind in payroll taxes, my life insurance had been canceled, and I was $250,000 in accounts receivable over 120 days because I did not know we needed to collect at the time of service, and *she* did not know we needed to send out statements. We were basically living on insurance payments.

Because I had lectured nationally, I knew most of the great practice management coaches on the circuit, and the best coach I knew was Linda Miles. I hired her to come in and turn my practice around. She was incredible, and taught me the importance of real systems, such as scheduling, marketing, and creating a superior team.

I also learned how to use practice monitors and know the numbers I needed to track, including understanding my profit and loss (P&L) statement. I hired a local bookkeeper to teach me how to use QuickBooks. I did my own QuickBooks for six months to better understand my overhead expenses and learn the ins and outs of QuickBooks. Then I hired the same local bookkeeper to come into my home office twice a month and enter all my personal and business numbers from my checkbook and credit card statements into QuickBooks. He also balances my checkbook and prints out all checks, including refunds. Each quarter he does my 941 federal tax return, state unemployment and state disability taxes and city taxes. I also had him set up QuickBooks $500-a-year payroll accounting program. This saved me from working with a payroll service at $2,000 a year, and it was much easier for my office manager to put in payroll hours. I pay my bookkeeper $36 an hour, and last year paid him $1,900 for my business and $600 for my personal accounting. He has a great knowledge of taxes and works very closely with my CPA. I have an excellent CPA who oversees everything, gives me advice, and does my tax returns for around $5,600 per year. She is very responsive, up to date, thorough and understands the IRS codes and makes me follow the rules.

I review the profit and loss statement and office production monitors monthly. You need to have good practice monitors which you can obtain from one of your fellow endodontist or a dental management coach. When you understand and monitor the numbers, there is less chance of embezzlement (staff-initiated bonus), an unfortunate but always real possibility. A two-doctor general dentistry practice in my town was embezzled for $1.9 million over seven years, and it can happen to you, if you don't know your numbers.

We hired new employees and an experienced administrative team member. I reduced the number of patients I saw, focused on enjoying each individual patient and the dentistry, and even got home on time. Within a month, I was much more profitable, doing procedures I loved.

Since that time, I've had many different practice management consultants come into my office, and every time it has been of great value. I have always had an interest in the business of dentistry and will share with you what I have learned from these consultants and what I have seen and learned from all the endodontic practices I have worked with over the past 20 years.

* * *

CREATING THE OFFICE CULTURE

The action of writing your vision is the most powerful way to make your new story happen. Once written and shared with the team, it becomes the culture of the practice. When writing about your new vision, think about the movie **Jerry McGuire** and check out the YouTube video "Jerry Maguire Mission Statement."

Write a vision statement describing how you want your practice to be. This process will start you thinking about what is important to you in your practice as you create your office culture. A vision shows the world your intent to change and starts you on your new path. A vision makes a strong statement to the world about who you are and where you are going. It is like a magnet that will bring into your life all the ideas, people, and tools you need to make it happen. It is also like a compass on a ship: it allows the captain to sail in a specific direction and helps guide the changes he needs to make to get to his new destination. Below is my own office vision statement, which I place at the front office where all patients can see.

My Office Vision: We are in a continual process of creating a story for our practice that is both fun and exciting and brings each of us personal fulfillment, joy, peace, and freedom. Through dedicated people, ideas, and the use of systems, we will develop a positive, nurturing, and safe environment to grow and fulfill our needs both personally and professionally. It will be a place of mutual respect, laughter, clear communication, and teamwork in an atmosphere that is fun, energized, and joyous. We will connect with our patients on a personal level and provide a patient "Wow" experience that it is so incredible that they will hesitate to leave our office for fear of entering a harsher world. Our office will have a reputation of high-quality treatment, being so gentle, safe, and caring that we will receive many new referrals from our existing patients. We will enjoy every day to the fullest and live in each moment. Our office will be filled with laughter, pride, a sense of ease, and a calmness that allows us to provide to each patient an experience that is unsurpassed.

* * *

CREATING AN EFFICIENT OFFICE

When I asked the average endodontist how long it takes them to complete a normal molar root canal, they usually say about one hour. That means in a nine-hour day they should be completing nine cases.

After looking at the numbers of thousands of endodontic practices, I have found that the average endodontist completes three to four cases a day, and if they can do seven treatments a day, they are in the top 10% of all endodontists in the country.

This number is simple to figure out. Take the number of cases you did last year and divide by the number of days you worked. The reason for this inefficiency is that most endodontists waste two to four hours a day doing paperwork and working on practice management. Many spend too much time on poorly designed schedules where emergency cases are next to productive cases and they don't have the time to complete their cases. We always recommend open space at the end of the day for emergencies that always become completed cases. Most doctors spend too much time on the phone or computer, on team-management issues, or just talking too much. Many doctors think that improving their techniques or the new equipment will increase net profit, but the real profitability is in efficient office systems and training the team to run those systems. Endodontists must focus on doing the dentistry and empower the team to manage the practice and stop spending four-to-six hours a week on practice management. If you empower your team to run your practice, you only need three to four hours per month for business management.

Many endodontists try to coach themselves, go to practice management seminars and then come back and try to train the team to change their system. The problem is they don't know which ones to change. That's why it is essential to have an on-site consultant observe office flow, the quality of the team members, and evaluate the systems that are not working, and recommend which systems need to be changed. They need to let go of all disruptive members of the team who cause unnecessary drama and frustration to the doctor and other team members. When systems really flow well, patients love being in the office, the team loves serving the patients, referrals go up, and endodontics becomes effortless—making the practice a lot of fun for everyone.

* * *

IDEAS AND SYSTEMS THAT CAN DOUBLE YOUR NET PROFIT

Phone Skills.

Today, most endodontists feel they just don't have enough patient flow and feel they need to spend more time on external marketing. The first phone call is where relationship building and marketing begins. Endodontists need to create an emotional connection with their patients and every referring office caller. Customer service must be our hallmark, just like it is at the Ritz-Carlton. To help train the office team in creating incredible patient relationships, go to the AAE.org website and then to the Endo on Demand section for videos of past AAE meetings. This area is a wealth of information to help you train your team. Select the speaker or type of training you need. For example, type in the name Judy Kay and her presentations on creating a WOW experience will come up. This can be used for a team training meeting or to help on board new team members.

Internal Marketing.

There are two basic types of referrals—internal and external. Internal referrals occur when you and your team can create an emotional connection with your patients while providing an efficient, painless and fun dental experience. It is important to always compliment the patient on their doctor and reinforce the referring doctor's treatment plan. I always personally say goodbye to the patient at the front desk before they leave and give them a token gifts of either pens, letter openers or chocolates. I compliment them on their bravery and in return they tell me that I did a good job. At that point I ask them to go back and tell their general dentist that they had a great experience. We will sometimes ask for Google or Yelp reviews if the appointment went exceptionally well and the patient was extremely happy.

* * *

CREATING AN EMOTIONAL CONNECTION WITH THE PATIENT.

This begins with the first phone call with the patient. It is about listening more and talking less. Each team member and the doctor need to be trained to ask more questions about the patient and talk less about themselves. Listening eases patient anxiety and signals that we're sincere. Sometimes patients are anxious because of their poor past dental experiences. Before I meet the patient, my assistant tells me that the patient is very nervous, so when I come into the room and introduce myself and tell them that I am very gentle. I will sit facing them and address their fears. I remind them that those fears from the past are embedded in their subconscious and they have no control of the fear when they come into the office. I also tell them that it takes great courage to face your fears and show up. Because of their courage, I will promise them three things: I will get them completely numb, they will always be in control, and I am very fast and efficient in my treatment delivery. This helps put the patient immediately at ease. Getting to know the patient is fun. Here is a thank you note from one of my patients that demonstrates the importance of emotional connection.

> Dear Dr. Goerig, two weeks ago I got a diagnosis of breast cancer stage IV. Two days after that I woke up with a swollen cheek and learned I needed a root canal and ended up in your chair. I was still emotionally reeling from my health news but noticed the poster from your time at Fort Knox Kentucky. I was stationed there as an Army dietitian and, when I shared all my story, you were so gracious, compassionate, and funny helping me relax and almost enjoying my time in your chair. Thank you for letting God use you to minister to me and reassure me of his love and care. You may not have been aware of it, but you were my angel that day! I still tear up thinking about it, how you verbally encouraged me, loved me

and encourage me further and then even reduced my charges, so I would not be facing such a huge bill. You are an angel and I can't thank you enough for being the conduit of God's love to me that day. I really needed it and won't ever forget it. God bless you and your whole family. With gratitude,

External Marketing.

Marketing works so well because most endodontists and other specialists just don't do it very well. It's key to the growth of your practice. Focus on different strategies and relationships that will return you an abundance of patients. One of my favorite quotes about marketing is, "Those who need to market should not, and those who don't need to market should." You aren't ready until you have everything in place in your office, have an incredible, caring team that can create the WOW experience, have a clean and up-to-date facility, are committed to seeing patients on time and completing on time, are clinically efficient and strive for perfection, and have the ability to see patients each day for emergencies. When these are in place, then you can start a vigorous marketing plan.

Most marketing plans fail because they are inconsistent and devote too little time to marketing. They have no marketing coordinator and very few strategies. The doctor does not spend much time creating relationships with the referring doctors and does not commit 2% to 3% of the revenue on marketing.

It is important to assign one of your administrative team members as a marketing coordinator responsible for implementing and managing the marketing program and strategies. Every endodontist needs to create a referral monitor to track the statistics monthly. I believe that you need to connect with your important offices each month. In my practice, we connect with eighty offices a month. The marketing coordinator will spend about twenty hours per month on these duties. I meet with the marketing coordinator and office manager once a month to review the statistics to ensure that the practice is headed in the right direction. If it's not, we identify ways to turn it around.

An Updated, Incredible Website.

This is one of the first places a referred patient will go to check you out. It must have good photos, good information and testimonials from your patients. It should be designed so that your website on your phone looks exactly like it does on the computer. It should have a patient-review area and a testimonial section. It is a good idea to have updated testimonials moving across the page so they can be easily seen. PBHS. com is one of the best companies that endodontists use for website design because of their layouts, patient survey system, videos and graphics.

Differentiation.

In marketing, it is better to be different than good. I strive to be both. Some of the ways that we differentiate ourselves from other endodontic practices is that we are open five days a week, understand various types and qualities of dental insurance, have available financing, have nitrous oxide and conscious sedation, are skilled at endodontic surgery, and have all the available updated technology. We also have team members fluent in Spanish. We have an incredible, loving, patient-oriented team that strives to provide an incredible patient experience. We perform single-appointment endodontics. We are generous with those in need.

Bonus System.

When I was in the Army, I would work very hard for three years in an assignment to get a ten-cent ribbon. This doesn't work as well in civilian life but showing your appreciation through bonuses and thanking them often pays big dividends. One of the most effective ways to increase profitability is to have a bonus system that highly motivate your team while it increases your net profit. To make a bonus effective, everyone on the team must understand how the bonus is calculated. It is much better to give a bonus on a daily or monthly basis instead of yearly to get more excitement and participation from the team.

Bonuses should be designed to reward the entire team, creating team synergy. All bonuses must be based on collections with the understanding that total team compensation should not exceed 18%. When you are trying to help your team get out debt, remind them that the bonuses can accelerate their debt reduction. There are many types of bonus systems; I recommend that bonuses be based on the number of extra completed cases per day. This is the easiest to track and understand. I feel the best and immediate bonus that you can give your team is to compliment them and thank them often for specific things such as filling the schedule properly, creating great relationships with your patients, and making same-day service work. I thank each of my team players individually for being part of our incredible team.

Adult Oral Sedation Dentistry.

Fear of dentistry is one of the main reasons why only 65% of the population goes to a dentist. Many of those with the greatest fears need extensive dental work done. Becoming certified in adult oral sedation gives you a great marketing advantage for those referring offices that have fearful patients who need endodontic treatment. The best course for dentists is provided by DOCS Education. It is by far one of the best courses I have ever taken. They also have an IV sedation certification course: https://www.docseducation.com; 855-227-6505

The Power of Observation to Improve Speed and Quality.

One of the fastest ways to increase clinical speed and improve quality, besides going to hands-on courses, is to observe a very efficient and high-quality endodontic practitioner. If you know any endodontists doing over seven cases per day, ask if you can observe them in their offices. You may want to video the procedure. Ask if you can bring your chief clinical assistant and front office team member to observe the flow of the practice. I personally know the power of observation because it is part of my Endo Mastery coaching program. Endodontists and their teams from all over the country visit my office four months into coaching. I guarantee you that they are looking at my clinical results, and I love showing how effortless it can be to produce high-quality treatments.

Twenty years ago, one young endodontist from California who was doing about $60,000 a month in his practice. After our consultant visited his office, he jumped up to $90,000 a month. Four months into our program, he came with his team to observe my office. It was not my endodontic technique that was important, but rather how everything effortlessly flowed around me, how the team related to patients, and how the front and back team made the schedule flow for high production. After the team returned the next month, they produced $162,000.

Another client was finishing up our coaching program and initially went from three cases to six cases per day but had trouble doing more. The week after visiting my office he did thirteen treatments and now averages ten cases per day—an increase in net profit of over $1 million. That is the power of observation. You just need to see it, and then things click. With the right systems, it is easier and less stressful to do six cases than three.

Creating Team Spirit.

As I said when discussing bonuses, the best and most immediate bonus that you can give your team is complimenting and thanking them often for specific things, such as filling the schedule properly, creating great relationships with your patients, and seeing and completing emergency patients the same day. I thank each of my team players individually. We build team spirit through going to the AAE national meeting, four-day cruises to Mexico or Disneyland. We celebrate team members birthday by going out to a restaurant for dinner. We go around the table and each team member tells that individual what they really like about her or him. This is very powerful.

Making the Office a Place of Safety and Peace.

I was talking to an endodontist who owned his practice and he was complaining about this one assistant who was consistently causing drama and stirring a negative pot in the practice. This had been going on for two years and he did not know what to do. I told him to go back to the practice and tell the owner to immediately fire that person. Then I reminded him that he was the owner. Let go of all employees who create drama in your practice. You cannot change people, but you can "change" people.To create and develop strong employee manual or to get help with employee issues, contact CEDR, contact CEDR solutions at https://www.cedrsolutions.com/ for advice and support.

Handling Clinical or Office Frustrations.

When things are not going exactly the way you want, don't get upset. Instead, laugh or use the following words and phrases to refocus and stay on task: great, next, isn't that interesting, or it is what it is. Frustration and anger are detrimental to obtaining high quality clinical results and creating a fun and profitable office.

Addressing negative family and cultural imprints about success.

Many dentists do stupid things with money because they have no formal training in financial matters. The biggest obstacles to fiscal prudence often stem from culture beliefs about money learned from our family. Some examples: you have to work hard to earn money; getting rich is a matter of luck; money is the root of all evil; when things are going good, they will always go bad. You may have felt unworthy as a child, and this imprint prevents you from being successful and profitable in your practice causing you to self-sabotage your success in practice and your investments. One of the hardest things I do as a coach is to help clients get past low-deserve levels embedded in their subconscious. This is true when investing their money. One purpose of this book is to give a simplified investment game plan that keeps them away from financial advisors, risky investments and other situations where they would lose money. I knew one doctor who continued to sabotage himself in his investments and practice. He fortunately got a great dental coach who helped him create incredible profitable practice. He was finally able to put enough money away so he could retire. After he sold his practice, he had all the money needed to enjoy a fun and exciting retirement. But his inner demons took over and he lost all his earnings in a real estate deal. Doctors who continually self-sabotage and do stupid things with money may find themselves living on Social Security in your children's home and taking vacations in a 200-mile radius.

If you have poverty-consciousness imprinting or a low-deserve level, you need to get professional help you break your behavioral patterns around money. One company that has helped many of my coaching clients is Legacy Life Consulting at https://www.legacylifeconsulting.com/. Create a story that allows you to expand your life and move out of your comfort zone.

Becoming a Stronger Leader.

The owner/doctor is responsible for writing the practice's vision based on his or her core values, which create the culture of the practice. When you are not leading and paying attention there will be much more drama in the team because they will have lost respect for you. Great leaders empower their team to lead, but each senior team member knows the vision and direction of the practice is coming from the doctor. Doctors will sometimes give up the leadership role because they're trying to be the nice guy and are conflict adverse. When the doctor gives up the leadership role, someone will fill the void. When you get clear and want to step back into the leadership role the person who has led the team will resent and feel under appreciated. This may end up in a dismissal of that great employee. Great leaders win hearts before minds. Leaders must be authentic and trust themselves, always learning and open to all possibilities for constructive and positive change. Read Simon Sinek book, *Start with Why: How Great Leaders Inspire Everyone to Take Action*. Here are a few ways to keep growing as a leader:

- Give up control—delegate and empower the team.
- Get out of the way—but follow up.

- Know the numbers (use practice monitors).
- Spend 98% of your time in direct patient care.
- Lead by example and be the best employee.
- Tell the team what you want.

UNDERSTANDING AND WATCHING THE BUSINESS NUMBERS

- These are some areas with which you should thoroughly familiarize yourself in your practice:
- Understand the daily cross-check system.
- Review the Accounts Receivable Report and Outstanding Insurance Claims with the appropriate team member.
- Complete and reviewing the monthly monitors.
- Review monthly referral trends.
- Review monthly production numbers with the office manager, chief clinical assistant, and marketing manager.
- Know how to use QuickBooks and print out, read, and understand a *Profit and Loss* statement.

Average Endodontic Overhead Expenses

- Team Compensation   16%–20%
- Facility   4%–7%
- Marketing   1%–3%
- Office Supplies   1%–2%
- Dental Supplies   6%–7%
- Other Operational Expenses   7%–11%
- TOTAL   35%–50%

Endo Mastery Case Study: Where did the money go?

A forty-two-year-old endodontist collected $1.1 million in 2017. He told me his overhead was 38%, which meant that he should have taken home $690,000. I asked him why his tax return showed that he only made $390,000, which would've been an overhead of 65%. I asked him what happened to the $300,000. *He did not know.*

These stories repeat themselves in many endodontic offices because we are not taught to understand the numbers. After investigation, we discovered he did not add up the items that were really part of his net profit. He donated to 401(k) plans, he paid off new equipment, he paid down debt service on the practice, some of his wages were included with the team wages, and he left money in his business account at the end of the year. And there is always the possibility of embezzlement, which I call "staff-initiated bonuses."

Accounts Receivable (AR).

The doctor must review the accounts receivable each month. A healthy AR should be 50% of the current months adjusted production. Adjusted production represents the money that is collectable after insurance adjustments have been made. If you take insurance, a good AR will be 50% or less than the current adjusted production. This means if your adjusted monthly production is $100,000, then you would have a total accounts receivable for the month should be around $50,000. If you're accounts receivable are greater than four weeks of adjusted production,, you need to act and get collecting. Another goal should be to have the ninety-day and over AR less than 6% of monthly collections.

How to Reduce Insurance Stress.

Working with patients' insurances can be very time-consuming and stressful. If you need to work with insurance companies, pick only the ones that pay you above 80% of your fee. If you are in a very competitive high insurance demographics and you have trouble filling your schedule each day, then you can go below 80% to fill your schedule. Check insurance benefits, or at least look on the internet to verify that they have insurance and the amount of their benefits remaining. There are many insurance companies that will keep you on the phone for a half hour waiting to see how much benefits have been used. We no longer do that in our office. We will either ask the patient or call the referring doctor to see how much of their benefits have been used. Learn and understand every insurance company criterion. Send out electronic claims using a company called Renaissance, which is only $49 a month for all claims.

If you're not familiar with the patient's insurance, you may want to have them pay you everything up front and submit their insurance or at least over-guesstimate their copay and be able to send them a refund. If you are in an area where there are a lot of insurance policies, then have someone like Becky Balok negotiate higher percentages for you. Becky@ bbdentalconsulting.com 602-908-8118

Small Practice Changes = Enormous Increases in Net Profit

It is amazing that you can increase your income by $520,000 a year by just doing two additional root canals per day. If your root canal fee is $1,300, then two root canals are $2,600. If you work 200 days a year (four days per week), that is the additional $520,000. This would increase your take-home net to $800,000 per year. There is no additional overhead associated with these extra two root canals. Your entire school loan debt, home and practice loan could be paid off in two years. Now that you are debt free, you will have three times the amount of money to be able to work less, invest, and enjoy your personal freedom. After coaching, one of my clients doubled his net profit that year and was able to pay off his $705,000 debt in just eighteen months!

	5 root canals per day		3 root canals per day	
	Amount	Over-head/ Profit %	Amount	Over-head/ Profit %
Collections	$1,300,000	100%	$780,000	100%
Overhead	$500,000	39%	$500,000	64%
Net profit	$800,000	61%	$280,000	36%
Daily collections	$6,500/day		$3,900/day	
Monthly collections	$108,333/month		$65,000/month	
4 days/ week worked	200 days/year with two weeks off			

FIGURE 5

Chapter 4:

RAISE YOUR FEES ANNUALLY

MANY ENDODONTISTS DO NOT get around to raising their fees annually or semiannually. I recommend that you routinely raise your fees 2% to 4% a year just to keep up with inflation and the rising cost of dental materials. Even though you are locked in by some insurance plans, you should routinely do this for all other patients.

Most owners do not understand the power of raising fees to increase net profit. If you have $100,000 per month practice and your overhead is 70%, your net profit would be $30,000 that month. A 10% increase in fees would give you an additional $10,000, and when added to your net of $30,000, you would have a total net of $40,000. This is a 33% increase in your profit.

Below is a chart that shows you how a 1%, 3% and 5% increase could affect the total net income of your practice over thirty years. Go to ADA.org/feesurvey to get a free 2018 fee guide for your area. These are free for ADA members. You can also purchase the updated fee guide for your ZIP Code from Wasserman-medical.com for $169. Try to keep fees that the patients call about in the eightieth percentile. Because of dental insurance companies' pressures, you cannot collaborate to set fees with other dentists, but you can ask them what their fee guide is and then make your own decision regarding what your new fees will be. You may also hire someone to negotiate your fees with your insurance companies. (Check out Becky Balok at www.bbdentalconsulting.com.)

INCREASED NET PROFIT BY INCREASING FEES				
Totals	Yearly Collections	Total Collections Increase		
		1% per year	3% per year	5% per year
30 years	$500,000	$2,556,370	$9,501,339	$19,880,395
30 years	$1 million	$5,112,740	$19,002,678	$39,760,790
30 years	$1.5 million	$7,669,110	$28,504,017	$59,641,185

Chapter 5:

HIRE A PRACTICE MANAGEMENT EXPERT

I COFOUNDED ENDO MASTERY IN 1996 with my brother-in-law Todd Holmes who was a senior executive at Hallmark cards. Initially the company's name was Inner Peace Seminars because so many endodontists were stressed in their practice and did not understand practice-management systems. I got some pushback from the name Inner Peace, which scared some people, so we renamed the company Endo Mastery. The philosophy of the company was the same—to create a practice that is profitable, fun, and efficient and allows much more time to spend with families while finding and maintaining peace. That is why our motto is "Transform your Practice, Transform your Life." We must all realize that there is a difference between making a living and making a life worth living.

* * *

"THE ACE PROCESS"

In 1992, I created a practice model where I worked about 120 days a year and took off a week each month. This is made possible by having an associate work with you in your practice. I initially called this the "retire in practice" model, but then many of my clients started calling it the "Ace Process." It begins with a beautiful vision, the right systems, scheduling, team, efficient techniques and marketing. With the increased profitability, most endodontists can be debt free within two to five years, even with $2 million in debt. Once the practice reaches $1.4 million, bring in an associate and work 130 days a year. This allows you to work three days a week. Having the associate work three or four days ensures the office is open five days a week. Most of my associates take home $600,000 to $750,000 per year working three days a week. They seem very happy and have no administrative responsibilities or headaches. The only other duties they have is to help market the practice.

The average endodontist collects around $750,000 a year and takes home $250,000 to $450,000 a year working four-to-five days a week. Our goal with our Endo Mastery clients is to have them reach the $1.4 million in collections and find a long-term associate who is not interested in ownership. They must be compatible and have the same treatment philosophy. This is essential in creating long-lasting committed referrals. When you earn anything less than $1.4 million, you take a significant reduction in your income and there is not enough money to adequately pay an associate doctor. Endo Mastery gets you the $1.4 million point and then helps you bring on an associate. We only hire doctors who want to be long-term associates and are not interested in ownership. After coaching, our doctors can net between $700,000 to $1,200,000 per year while working three days a week with one associate.

When you work fewer days, you are more refreshed, perform higher quality treatment, and enjoy the practice more. You create an empowered team that runs the practice even when you're not there, but you maintain complete control. You have time to focus on your family, hobbies and health. We also help you reprogram your negative belief that you need to work hard for a living. As you progress in this process, you will understand the secret of happiness and loving life.

For twenty years, I worked Monday and Tuesday and had Wednesday off for vacation, then worked Thursday and had Friday, Saturday, and Sunday off for vacation. And then, every four to six weeks, I took a week off for vacation. Now I work only two days a week and feel like I'm on vacation all the time. This can only occur if you have an associate with the same philosophy.

In our culture, retirement indicates old age, or it's seen as a reward for working hard for forty years. I do not buy into this old concept. By my definition, retirement is the time of many choices, opportunities and excitement. I believe you can begin your retirement when you're young through the concept of "retire in practice." This happens when you become debt free, which allows you unlimited choices for your life. I have coached many endodontists who became debt-free within two-to-three years and some became debt free in their thirties. Then they brought in an associate allowing them to work 130 days a year. We can always make more money, but we can never make more time in our life. What message are you sending your children about how to live life? Give them the example of what real retirement (choices) looks like throughout your life.

Even though your practice is a constant source of income and can allow you to work as many days as you want, there may be a time when you want to sell your practice, work one or two days a week, or just walk away. There is no right answer, but you do have choices and the time to figure out what works best for you. You and your spouse need to create this story together.

The "Ace Process," or the "retire in/out of practice," is modeled below.

RETIRE IN/OUT OF PRACTICE MODELS				
	Working	Retire in Practice 1	Retire in Practice 2	Retire Out of Practice (remote controlled practice)
Practice Type	Solo Owner works 4-5 days/ week (190 to 225 days/ year)	Owner works 3 days/ week with one associate (130 days per year)	Owner works 2 days/ week with multiple associates (90 days per year)	Team managed with multiple associates and non-producing owner (0 days per year)

FIGURE 6

Why become an associate in an Endo Mastery office?

Many new graduates start out as associates because their debt prevents them from obtaining a practice loan. They may work as an associate in an endodontic practice or corporate office four to five days a week with only a few weeks of vacation a year, and only earning between $150,000 to $300,000 per year. After taxes, it will take years for them to eliminate their school debt and pay off their home. In some of these endodontic practices, they earn even less because there is not enough patient flow to fill the associate's schedule. Corporate offices may have plenty of patients on low-fee plans, resulting in more cases but lower collections and income for the associate. In many corporate offices, the associate will often travel some distances to work in multiple corporate offices during the week. They may have to bring their own microscopes to each location. Many of these corporate offices will entice new associates with signing bonuses, benefits and a guaranteed income, which last only for the first three months, after which their income can be substantially reduced if the associate does not meet their production goal.

A better choice is to work for an endodontic practice that has been coached through Endo Mastery. These are usually single-doctor endodontic practices in great locations with a strong referral base. An associate starts at around $300,000 per year with the opportunity to make somewhere between $600,000 and $700,000 per year. The goal of these practices is to help increase the associate's efficiency over time so they can eventually earn $600,000 to $700,000 per year in a stress-free office while working three or four days a week and taking eight-to-ten vacation weeks off a year.

As an associate in these practices, you will have the clinical freedom and autonomy enjoyed in a traditional private endodontic practice without the additional financial and administrative burdens associated with practice management, personnel and salary issues, billing, accounts receivable or other headaches of owning an office. You will spend 95% of your time in direct patient care but still have input in the decision-making of the office. This allows you to spend more time with your family and do the things you love, offering you the luxury of a better work/life balance.

There are some endodontic practices owners who are exhausted and stressed in their practice and are only taking home around $250,000 a year working four days a week. Many of these owners could sell their practice and work for an Endo Mastery coaching office. They can take the profit from their practice, pay off debt or invest in their retirement and become an associate without any headaches with the possibility of making up to $600,000 per year working three days a week in an Endo Mastery coached practice. Endo Mastery clients are located throughout the country.

Why We Need Time Off.

Most endodontist see vacation and time off as a reward for working hard, but I see vacations as a time of rejuvenation and creativity. It is amazing how creative you can be, developing new ideas to improve your relationships, your practice and maximize your productivity, when you are sitting on the beach in Maui, like I am now doing while completing this book. Most endodontists only take three to four weeks off a year and are working four or five days a week. Coming back from vacation, doctors are much more productive; unless they get another vacation within six weeks, they may move into the mechanical stage of treatment, and production declines. Over time, this routine can lead to burnout. That is why I am a big proponent of not working more than two days in a row.

What can coaches do for the practice?

Coaching is about implementation, interpretation, observation and hands-on guidance. Coaches are trained, outside observers with insights and experience to help illuminate your blind spots and encoded limitations while providing you with specific steps and systems to get the results you desire. Knowledge is not power—it is potential power. Without action, nothing happens. The key is implementation. To do this effectively, you do need a coach.

You must ask two questions after trying to change all the problems and stress in your practice by yourself: How is what you are doing now working, and what is the true value of time with your family and for yourself worth? Coaching helps you gain peace of mind and create your freedom. Below is a short list of what the endodontists we coach have wanted to improve in their practice and a list of the most stressful areas of their practice.

What would you like to improve in your practice?

- Maximizing the use and effectiveness of technology.
- Practice management.
- I need help training and leading the office staff.
- I need help keeping track of the business numbers and my referrals.
- I need the office to be more profitable.
- Help me stop practice profitability from declining.
- More efficient scheduling/productive days.
- Increase referral numbers/implement a consistent marketing program and tracking.

- Less stress on me/have others in office do more/doctor do mostly dentistry.
- Bringing in an associate.

What causes you the most stress about your practice?

At the beginning of our coaching year I have a three- to four-hour freedom summit webinar with each coaching client, spouse and their individual coach. One area I am concerned about is the causes of the greatest stress in their practice. I also ask them, on a scale from one to ten, how stressed and exhausted they are at the end of the day. Most tell me seven to ten. Here are some issues these doctors were stressed about:

- Difficult patients and cases
- Holes in the schedule
- Team problems
- Schedule stress
- Running behind
- Broken instruments
- Cash flow problems
- Paperwork
- Calls with patients and doctors
- Administrative challenges
- Feeling overworked

By modifying a few things in a practice, an endodontist can often double their net profit, reduce stress and have more time off. Having systems in place to schedule patients more efficiently, collecting fees at the time of service, emphasizing efficient scheduling, and raising fees are all examples that significantly increase the bottom line without raising overhead.

Ten Traits of a Successful Endodontic Practice

In the coaching process we help the doctor and the team become masters in these areas:

1. Leadership of the team not only from the doctor but from the office manager and each of the leaders of the clinical team and the front office team.

2. Scheduling that creates a smooth and efficient flow of patients throughout the day, reducing no-shows and cancellations while being able to fill in open appointment times.

3. Creating an incredible team through proper hiring, training and incentive programs. Having each team member committed to the office vision, the patient, the referring office and the doctor.

4. The doctor develops excellent clinical skills allowing the him/her to focus on the patient and flow effortlessly through the day.

5. The doctor and team creating an emotional connection with patients and referring offices.

6. Strong communication skills up-and-down the team.

7. The doctor understands the important numbers of their endodontic practice.

8. A powerful marketing program orchestrated by a well-trained marketing coordinator resulting in a high number of referrals each month.

9. The office is up to date, clean, and provides a safe and warm environment for every patient.

10. Most importantly, team members have fun in the practice and enjoy everything they do.

Endodontics Is in Crisis.

Today, endodontics is in a crisis from many external forces, and unless we understand and change the business model, more small practices will continue to decline. We need to be able to see patients that day and complete cases that day. We need to be open five days a week so the referring doctors can always get their patients in that day.

If we can do this, the general dentist will stop doing root canals and we will have all the patients we need as well as easier cases. This is called the "Ace Process."

Endodontics Is Always Changing.

Endodontics has changed considerably just over the twenty-seven years I have been in private practice. When I first started, I was booked out over three months. Today, we fill the schedule day by day. But the advantage is that we get easier cases from emergencies. We now have all this new technology and motorized instrumentation that gives us much more predictable results. Before rotary instrumentation, my fingers were so sore I had trouble buttoning my shirt just by doing six cases a day.

In 1992 John McSpadden invited me out to Chattanooga, Tennessee, to show me his new Maxim files, one of the first nickel titanium rotaries. Dr. Schick put one of the first digital radiographs in my office in 1992. I was one of the first to get the Zeiss Jena microscopes and ultrasonics from Gary Carr. I consider John McSpadden and Gary Carr Renaissance men in endodontics. I was the first endodontist in my town to have the CBCT scan. I also have the Gentle Wave which I use on selective cases. This new technology has made endodontics continually fun and exciting.

In this process of change, many forces cause endodontist stress. They can be either external or internal forces. Some of the external forces over which we have no control are more corporate offices, increase in overhead due to insurance companies controlling fee increases, more endodontists, less endodontists retiring, more general dentists doing endodontics, implants instead of retreatments and, of course, the big one is all the retail shopping and vacations our patients take instead of doing needed dentistry. We need to learn to stop stressing over things we cannot control and focus on what we can control!

I never worry about the other endodontists in town as I see them as colleagues not competition and I always wish them the best. Abundance comes in your life by remaining open to sharing and supporting others in your community. If my practice slows, I accelerate my marketing efforts. I am in a town of 100,000 people with eight endodontists, and our referral area is just over 200,000. Yet we are very busy because we trained the general dentist in the area to send more cases because we can treat them right away. They stop doing root canals. I work two days per week, my partner works three days, and my son works four days a week in the practice. Even with just nine doctor days per week, we are one of the most profitable endodontic practices in the country because of our systems. To be able to continue this type of referral intensity in a town that I've been in for over twenty-seven years requires doing quality cases and providing excellent patient care.

Things we can control are the internal forces, such as lower production and doctor compensation, fewer patients, tougher cases and open schedules, no-shows and last-minute cancellations, student debt, increase in office drama, and overwhelming administrative challenges. If your practice is not growing, it is declining. Over 70% of all endodontic practices have declined over the past few years.

Many endodontists are frustrated and stressed in their practice. They think a practice-management course will solve their problems. But the real problem is they don't know what needs addressing. Many doctors spend too many hours trying to control their practice. The most important service a practice-management consultant can provide is to help you determine which issues are holding you back and correct the systems and team issues.

* * *

ENDO MASTERY EXAMPLES

The *Death Wish* Endodontist.

I got a call from a fifty-eight-year-old endodontist who wanted my advice about his practice. For the past thirty years he worked five days a week and traveled one hour each way to work and back. He was producing around $900,000 and taking home around $279,000. He was exhausted and wanted more time off. He asked if it was a good idea to bring in an associate, which reminded me of a movie called Death Wish.

I told him that bringing in an associate with only $900,000 production would reduce his net profit by half, and the associate would not stay because there was not enough production to pay the associate an adequate income. Then he suggested opening another office between his home and his current office. This reminded me of the movie Death Wish 2. I am rarely a fan of multiple offices because you must develop two completely different referral sources, and because when you are in two locations you cannot adequately be available for those referring doctors who will go elsewhere. I suggested to the doctor that we work with him in our coaching program to increase his production to $1.4 million before bringing in an associate. The associate would work three or four days, and the endodontist would be able to cut down to three days a week with eight to ten weeks off for vacation. He would make more money, be less stressed and have much more time off. He said he would think about it. That was over four years ago.

Endo Mastery Case 1:

Missed Opportunity. In 2014 an endodontist called me and asked about my coaching program. I told her the fee and she said that was just too much to spend on consulting. I did tell her that the next month I had a two-day course offering a lot of information without going through the coaching program. She said she would think about it but never signed up.

At that same course, another endodontist from the same small community signed up for our coaching program. He had been an associate after graduating in 2001, and in 2012 he did a startup practice. He was averaging about three cases a day, producing about $3,800. He was working five-and-a-half days a week and was getting tired. He wanted to make sure his practice was successful and that he could pay off his large debt. Within one month after visiting his office, he increased his cases to five treatments a day, and within six months he was doing seven to nine cases per day, resulting in a daily production of $12,000 to $14,000. One day he did over $20,000. During that year he increased his net profitability from $300,000 to $1.3 million—over one million extra dollars per year to pay off debt. The coaching might have been worth it. Within three years he was debt free and will be financially free in seven years. He now has a full-time associate and works three to four days a week. Many are willing to listen, but few are ready to hear.

Endo Mastery Case 2:

Female Endodontist Challenges. An endodontist who just graduated two years, before came to one of our meetings and signed up for our coaching program. She told us that she wanted to improve her practice, perform endodontics more efficiently, and reduce her overhead and debt. She was completing about three-and-a-half treatments a day and was working 220 days a year. She and her team were completely open to our coaching process. Within two months she was doing six cases a day, and by the end of the coaching year she was up to eight-and-a-half cases a day, working 165 days a year. The next year, she had a difficult pregnancy and reduced her days in the office to 110 days, during which time she delivered a beautiful healthy baby. The days she was in the office, she completed an average of nine to ten cases a day and collected over $1.4 million that year. She hired an associate, allowing her to work 120 days per year. She is out of debt and continues with our Mastery Circle study club.

Endo Mastery Case 3:

Increased Marketing. Three years ago, we coached an endodontist in the Northeast who had been in practice for eleven years and wanted to increase her efficiency and decrease her stress. Patient flow had fallen off and so had her production. Her main emphasis was to help increase patients to fill up her schedule. The year before, she was working 182 days a year doing about three cases per day and collecting around $800,000. We changed her schedule to make it much more efficient, thereby reducing the stress in the office. She increased her cases to seven treatments a day, and her yearly production was $1.5 million while reducing her days in the office to 141. She is now working on bringing in an associate and reducing the days in the office to spend more time with her family and to take care of herself. She continues with our Mastery Circle study club.

Endo Mastery Case 4:

New Endodontic Graduate. In 2003, a recently graduated endodontist came to me and said his wife told him that he needed my coaching program. He was thirty-two years old. He opened a new practice and during our program, we helped him hire a great team and develop an efficient schedule and taught him the ins and outs of marketing. Initially, he was completing three to four cases a day, as do most recent graduates. By the end of our coaching year, he was completing seven to eight cases, working an eight-hour day. He used the dental operating microscope 100% of the time.

With the increased profitability, we encouraged him to get out of debt as soon as possible. He followed that advice and by 2008 was thirty-seven years old and debt free. Within two years we helped him bring in an associate so he could be open five days a week and reduce his working days to three days a week. That year he worked 130 days and began his retirement in practice while taking home over seven figures a year. He now has two associates and works only two days a week. As with all practices, teams change, things become routine, and sometimes there might be declines in referrals and profitability. Whenever he noticed this, he brought us in for another year of coaching to retrain the office, increase profitability and referrals, and help keep them on track. He continues to be a member of the Mastery Circle.

Endo Mastery Case 5:

Sixty-Two-Year-Old Endodontist. An endodontist that I knew out of my residency called me and was exhausted and stressed out. He had a bad partnership, was working five days a week and, because of some poor money decisions could not retire. He was driving forty minutes to his practice and back from his home. He had two locations and was doing about three to four cases a day in a drama-filled office. His younger partner and he were always arguing. He was tired and exhausted and didn't know what to do.

We worked with the office to increase profitability and then recommended that they break up their partnership and each one takes an office. I worked with my friend and, within a year, he was completing six cases a day and, within two years, eight. We helped him find an associate so he could reduce the time in the office to only three days a week. Because of his increased income, he could pay down his debts. He is now thinking of selling his practice and working as an associate two day a week closer to his home. With the sale of the practice, he can create a good investment portfolio and probably never touch it as long as he is loving what he is doing as an associate. It is amazing how outside guidance can make circumstances change so quickly to allow us peace of mind and financial freedom.

***

ENDO MASTERY RESULTS

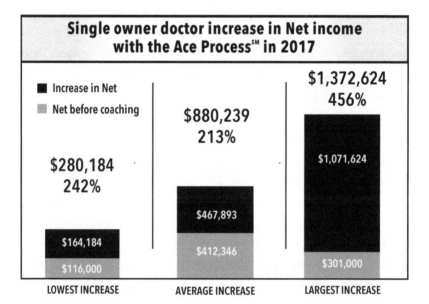

The average increase in our 2017 clients' production was $467,893, or eight times their investment with the Ace Process. Coaching is not an expense. Rather, it's a guaranteed investment with extremely high returns. If the doctor continues to keep the same increase each year, in ten years the return on investment would be $4,678,930. The smallest increase was $164,184, which gave that doctor an almost two-and-a-half increase in net profit. The average net income grew two times to $880,239. The highest increase of one doctor was over $1 million during that one year. See the chart below.

Sixty percent of Endo Mastery clients continue for another year or until they reach their desired goals such as bringing in an associate or being able to work two or three days a week. Many of them continue to work with Endo Mastery continued basis at a reduced rate, so they can focus on patient care while Endo Mastery focuses on the numbers and practice management. Below are examples of the increase over a four- and five-year period showing the yearly increase compared to their yearly collections before coaching. Also, note the total of increased net collections over those years.

Dr.	Before coaching collections	Collection increase each year from the original base collections					Total collection increase
		2014	2015	2016	2017	2018	
A	$494K		$117K	$310K	$512K	$706K	$1.65M
B	$734K		$381K	$545K	$603K	$720K	$2.25M
C	$1.22M	$200K	$354K	$529K	$654K	$953K*	$2.69M
D	$912K	$284K	$396K	$823K	$980K	$1.01M	$3.49M
E	$740K	$251K	$543K	$835K	$1.38M*	$1.68M**	$4.69M
F	$925K	$289K	$740K	$892K	$2.05M*	$2.40M*	$6.37M
F	$973K	$556K	$1.24M*	$1.07M	$1.48M	$2.17M*	$7.48M

Years of *1 associate ** 2 associates

Why is Endo Mastery coaching different than any other consulting programs?

- We work exclusively with endodontists and have a working endodontic model based on one of the most successful endodontic practices in the country.
- We teach you to understand the numbers of the endodontic office.
- Each program is individualized, not "cookie cutter."
- We come to your office. Minimal loss of production time.
- Observational over-the-shoulder visits to Dr. Goerig's practice.
- Money-back guarantee.
- We are also about getting out of debt as well as personal and financial freedom.
- We work with a limited number of offices (sixty per year).
- Clinical efficiency mentoring is offered.
- You will have the opportunity to be invited into our Mastery Circle study club.
- Extensive video library on endodontic technique tricks to include videos of mastery circle clients complete over ten cases per day.
- Direct access to me and my personal cell phone number.

Areas that will be covered during your coaching program:

- Creating value for your patients and referring doctors.
- Scheduling and office flow.
- Scripting (verbiage) to prevent Cancellations, no shows and nontreatment.
- Office communication.
- How to present and collect fees at the time of service.
- Hiring, motivating and keeping a great team.
- Internal and external referral marketing.
- Creating an incredible patient WOW experience.
- Painless, effortless and efficient quality endodontics.
- Simplified monitors to track and understand the numbers.

- Business systems.
- Getting out of debt and steps to create financial and personal freedom.

How does the Endo Mastery coaching process work?

- It begins with a three-to-four-hour freedom summit with Dr. Goerig and your coach to review your key performance indicators and establish a goal for the practice for the year.
- We send you manuals and videos covering scheduling, marketing, hiring, and the training of the front clinical team.
- We immediately set up and help you implement the Endo Mastery daily monitor and referral tracking monitors.
- At that time, we set up a two-day office visit to evaluate all office systems, flow of the office, and the functioning of your team. The twelve-month coaching clock starts at this time.
- We train your team on Endo Mastery monitors and systems.
- There are monthly face-to-face webinars with you and your team leaders. Initially we may be working with you every week to help you with the flow of the schedule.
- You have access to our coaching member's website, which has many videos and documents on our practice management techniques.
- After you have been in our program for four or five months, you will come to my office for an over-the-shoulder training session. Once you leave the practice, you may increase your cases completed by two or even three per day.
- You have direct access to your coach and Dr. Goerig at all times.

Mastery Circle

After finishing the first year of coaching, clients are invited into the Mastery Circle. This is a fellowship of many of our past and active coaching endodontists who have similar strong core values and are committed to continued personal and professional growth. You also have access to the Mastery Circle member website, which has extensive videos, audios, and practice management and marketing ideas that have been shared by me and other Mastery Circle members. I presents monthly webinars on updated subjects of interest.

There are two, two-day meetings a year where we all share the best things we learned over the year in our practice and life. One is just for doctors, and the second meeting includes the office manager, chief clinical assistant, front office lead and the marketing coordinator. This is an opportunity for them to learn from others in their same leadership role. We bring in outside speakers to amplify the learning experience. This synergistic approach to learning and sharing helps us all grow exponentially and allows each of us to reach greater heights of personal excellence, peace and freedom. These meetings have an atmosphere of friendship and camaraderie that is safe and supportive, no egos allowed. These meetings help us create a bigger story and better quality of life for ourselves and all other people who are in our lives.

Coaching Is an Investment.

Warren Buffett said, "Invest as much in yourself as you can. You are your best asset. Most people go through their lives using a very small amount of their potential. Anything that you do to invest in yourself is the best investment you can possibly make." Why would anyone want to spend money on a dental consultant? The main reason, of course, is that what you're doing right now is not working. Doing more of it just becomes more frustrating and exhausting. I think the big reason many endodontists resist is that they are afraid to give up control of the practice. You must see coaching as a one-year MBA in endodontic management that is a guaranteed, risk-free investment. Our clients receive three- to fourteen-times return on investment (ROI). And remember that Uncle Sam is paying 35% to 50% of your investment. And if you have a partner, you can split the investment with them. Most doctors pay it off in the first three to four months with increased collections. But the real question: What is your family, time and freedom worth?

Is coaching right for you?

Very few endodontist see coaching as an investment that can give them over a 1,000% ROI. Many more will sign up for help when they have had enough pain. One famous quote is, "Change occurs when the pain to remain the same exceeds the fear to change." If you are not ready to be open to new systems, let go of control and empower your team, and are unable to fire a bad employee, or think you already know the answer, then you are not ready for coaching. Working with a coach requires the willingness to implement positive change from both you and your team. But if you can face your fears and be open to change, the rewards are many. The greatest reward is your freedom in your personal and professional life. Transform your practice and you transform your life.

Chapter 6:

LEARN HOW TO INVEST SAFELY AND SIMPLY

ONCE YOU ARE DEBT-FREE, you need to know the safest places to invest your money without high risk and without management fees. This part of the book will give you a specific game plan to reach your investment goals. The greatest return on your investment always comes first from paying off debt and becoming more profitable in your practice. The next safest and guaranteed investment is in the creation of a Prersonal Bank using a specialized whole life insurance policy that gives you a consistent guaranteed 4 percent plus return tax free. This is discussed in chapter 8. Investing in the stock market may provide a higher nonguaranteed taxable return but is more volatile with higher risks. The return can be significantly increased when you learn to eliminate fees by investing on your own through one of companies such as Schwab or Vanguard which I will discuss in chapter 7.

Disclaimer

I have found the following investment information to be helpful. I am not engaged in rendering professional services. If you require personal assistance or advice, seek a competent professional. I specifically disclaim any responsibility for any loss, liability, or risk, personal or otherwise, which is incurred therefore directly or indirectly of the use and application of the contents of this book.

Many endodontist get confused with investing and just do not understand how easy it is to invest on their own through a company like Schwab or Vanguard. That is why they are so vulnerable to investment schemes and high-fee advisors and brokers. In this chapter I will give you the secret to simple investing. More in-depth detail will be found in chapters 7 and 8.

When I first started coaching endodontist, I knew debt reduction and financial freedom were important. I also knew that people could achieve financial freedom easily. I had grand dreams about how I could make a big difference in people's lives. I developed the financial freedom guide through which they could accumulate gigantic amounts of money, and I showed them a sure and safe path to financial freedom. I had the illusion that in this way I could help my clients commit themselves to a safe economic pathway and change their lives.

I soon became discouraged, because many of my clients and their CPAs, brokers and financial advisors made a mess out of my finely designed plans. Instead of paying off debt, these "helpers" encouraged dentists to take their money and buy wasteful and unnecessary whole life insurance policies, risky stocks, hedge funds, annuities and speculative real estate. They put their clients' assets in actively managed mutual funds that took 3% to 4% of their return for themselves, resulting in a 60% to 70% loss of return that could have been made for my clients.

The losses were in the millions of dollars in my clients' investment portfolios, thus preventing geometric progression of their retirement plans, and undermining my advice.

We seem to have an infinite capacity to stress ourselves, especially when it comes to money. To a large degree, this comes from greed and ego. I knew one dentist who took his entire retirement plan of $300,000 and put it into a limited partnership. He did not really understand the potential risks and rewards, and he had no control over them. Within one year, he lost his entire retirement nest egg that had taken him twenty years to earn. I know a very smart and skilled chiropractor friend who got involved in a "Bernie Madoff"-type scheme and lost his entire savings of $1.3 million that took him twenty years to accumulate.

I teach from my own life experiences and have probably made every financial mistake in the book, including day trading, buying an oil well over the phone for $5,000 that disappeared in a few months, buying timeshares, and buying land where I was never going to live. From my many life experiences, financial misadventures and my work as a dental coach and financial mentor, I have developed a consistent philosophy and a guide of investing that can work for anyone.

In my money context, I want to reach financial freedom as safely and quickly as I can. People have a wide range of economic strategies. Some spread out their money and lose it by placing it into various so-called investments such as unnecessary life insurance policies, risky stocks, hedge funds and speculative real estate, commodities, day trading, and limited partnerships, hoping they will strike it rich. For most endodontist, these strategies are not efficient or reliable. Another strategy some people use is to reduce the amount of taxes they pay. Personally, I know that the more taxes I pay, the more money I am making. But Americans have a history of hating taxes. One of the things that pushed us into the American Revolution was taxation by England without representation. So, it's not surprising that one popular economic program revolves around avoiding taxes. In the 1970s and 1980s, there were tax shelters that were really taxes in disguise.

Some people are so busy avoiding taxes that they lose sight of the goal of financial freedom. Some people buy larger houses than they need so they'll have more interest to write off on their taxes. Saving money on taxes is inappropriate if it costs more money than it saves.

Everyone in this country could become financially free if they spent less than they made, or made more than they spent, got out of debt and invested the difference in safe, liquid assets. But if numbers and the idea of self-investing confuses you, this next paragraph will summarize all you need to know about successful investing. For a more in-depth understanding of investing, risk management and investment options, go to chapters 7 and 8.

**

DR. ACE'S FINANCIAL FREEDOM GUIDE
SIMPLE INVESTING SUMMARY

Make more money in your practice (use a coach) and focus all that money toward debt reduction. Once you are debt-free, your assets such as your business or your home act like a long-term inflation adjusted bond that can be used to obtain a line of credit or a source of our income. The next safest form of investment is creating a Personal Bank. This is a specially designed dividend paying whole life insurance policy where most of your premiums go into a rider that accelerates your growth of your equity and cash value in the policy (chapter 8). To check this out, go to chapter 8 and PersonalBank4u.com. The plan reduces the commission the advisor receives by 70% to 85% and you will have up to 90 times more cash value especially in the early years then with a traditional whole life policy. Because of the lower commission, most insurance agents do not offer this policy. These policies offer guaranteed tax-free growth and safety for your principal investment regardless of the ups and downs of the stock market or the economy. You will be able to use it as a financial management tool right from the beginning. This policy provides you tax-free access to your money for purchases, disability income or tax-free money for your retirement years giving you guaranteed growth that you can count on. The policy provides peace of mind and an income-tax-free legacy that you can pass on to your loved ones and/or favorite charities without going through probate. This is one of the safest, no risk investment for dentists.

The next option which involves risk is investing in the stock market. The reason that many investors do not do very well is that they rely on advisors or mutual fund companies that take 1% to 4% of your return resulting in a 50% to 70% loss of your overall investment return. Today, it is easy to invest on your own and eliminate these advisory and mutual fund fees.

In this book you will see how easy it is to create a Schwab account or a Vanguard account and learn how to invest on your own. Both these companies have great salaried advisors who will teach you how to invest on your own, step-by-step. Many of the "helpers" (brokers and financial advisors that you may have now) provide complicated investing strategies with multiple investment choices or investment theories such as Modern Portfolio Design, so you will think that investing is complicated and too hard for you to do alone. So, you pay them high fees, even though their returns are less than the S&P 500 or US stock index. William Bernstein said, *"You are engaged in a life-and-death struggle with the financial service industry. Every dollar in fees, expenses, and spreads you pay them comes directly out of your pocket. Act as if every broker, insurance salesman, mutual fund salesperson and financial advisor you encounter is a hardened criminal, and stick to low cost index funds, and you'll just do fine."* So, don't fall for that scam.

I was talking with my good dentist friend who had just recently married a beautiful lady whose husband died three years before. She related a story of a broker she went to for help with her investments which she knew little about. She was still dazed and confused from her loss and took all the funds she had gathered from selling homes, cars, dental practice and closing accounts. In December 2012, she gave the broker all her assets and asked him to "Manage this, be conservative, thank you."

He immediately placed her in an "actively managed account" and charged a 1% "wrap fee" annually, PLUS there were fees inside the account, e.g. front-end loads on mutual funds and high annual fees on mutual funds! In mid-2014, my friend and his new wife tried to get a handle on her returns, fees and commissions. They asked the financial advisor three questions: What was the returned in the managed portfolio in 2013? (Answer, +plus 5%.) What was the S&P 500 return for 2013? (The answer was plus 32.31%.) The third question was, how much were the total fees charged for the managed the portfolio for 2013? (The answer $28,000.00!) This story is not uncommon in the brokerage world and demonstrates why we need to understand the simple concepts of investing safely.

If you are with a financial advisor or a mutual fund company that is charging you more than $1,000 to $4,000 per year, you are paying too much and should transfer assets to Schwab or Vanguard into a low-cost index funds. Remember that a 1% to 2% fee could reduce your retirement assets, so you will have to work another ten years. I personally use Schwab because they are open twenty-four hours a day, seven days a week, have no minimum balance to open an account, and all trades within their funds and ETFs are free. All other trades, no matter what the amount, are $4.95. This is a great place to put your children's money: Roth IRAs. Both Schwab and Vanguard make it very easy for you to transfer assets from your overpriced mutual fund company and advisor into their company.

Most of us do not like confrontation with our past advisor when we try to transfer our assets. But it becomes very easy when you call up a Schwab representative and fill out the forms to have your assets automatically transferred into your new Schwab account. You don't even need to talk to your former advisor. To avoid the higher fees in your old company when you sell a stock or heavily loaded mutual fund, have the assets transferred to Schwab first, and then sell them for only $4.95. When you transfer your account, ask for twenty free trades for opening your account. There may be a few mutual funds that they cannot transfer over, and those will need to be sold into cash at your former brokerage house.

Now determine how much you need to diversify into US stocks, international stocks and bonds. This will depend on your risk tolerance and other factors. Chapters 7 and 8 will help you narrow your list of best individual asset allocation between bonds and stocks. For example, all you need to buy in your stock portfolio is the low-cost S&P 500 or total US stock market index mutual fund or ETF as described below. Then you're done.

Just buy the US market, which means the S&P 500 or the total US stock market mutual fund. Because there are always ups and downs in the market, wait until after there is at least a 10% drop in the market before you buy. If the market drops more, continue to buy. You can buy the Schwab S&P 500 index mutual fund (ticker symbol SWPPX) at the expense ratio of 0.03%, or the Vanguard 500 index mutual fund (ticker symbol VFIAX) with an expense ratio of 0.04%, both returning an average annual return over a ten-year period of about 15.3% and an average annual return over a fifteen-year period of 8.8%. Or you can buy Schwab US Broad Total Market index mutual fund (ticker symbol SWTSX) at the expense ratio of 0.03%, or the Vanguard Total Stock Market Index mutual fund (ticker symbol VTSAX with an expense ratio of 0.04%, both returning an average annual return over a ten-year period of 15.3% and an average annual return over a fifteen-year period of 9%.

Each month automatically transfer a set amount of money from your bank to your Personal Bank and Schwab or Vanguard money market account. Always stay in the market, and never sell, especially when the market drops: this is the time to buy more index funds, not sell. Today, in April 29, 2019, the markets again are moving up to all-time highs. This is not the time to buy into the market. Remember the adage about buy low and sell high. I personally like to keep my money my Personal Bank cash value and some in my Schwab money market account and take advantage of market drops throughout the year that are greater than 10%, as occurred in 2018, and buy the S&P 500 or the US stock market index using your money market account. Stop listening to the news and what's happening in the economy or the market. This is just noise. Don't even open your monthly investment statements. If you want to have a 401(k) plan for your office, go to America's Best 401(k) plan. That's it — you're done. Now enjoy your life.

I know that an all-stock portfolio as the S&P 500 index fund sounds risky but because of recent low interest rates, the ten years' total bond funds returns averaged 3.4%, international stocks averaged 6.6%, and the S&P 500 averaged 13%. History has always shown that the S&P 500 index has had a consistently higher return over time as compared to bonds and international stocks. This is the fastest way to become financially free. If you want high returns, you are going to invest in stocks (S&P 500) and occasionally experience losses in the market—but only if you sell—and if you want safety you're going to invest in bonds and endure low returns.

When you are working, your steady income is like having a bond portion in your portfolio. Also your paid off debt such as your home, your practice, and you're building are like a long-term inflation adjusted bond that is not affected by market corrections. Your Personal Bank and these assets provide a source of emergency money through home-equity loans or lines of credit. Your income and these inflation protected assets allows you to invest 100% into equities (S&P 500) for the long term, which will give you the greatest rate of return.

We are not smart enough to beat the market, but all we need to do is match the market. Long term, you may never need to touch your retirement principle and live off the dividends and interest. If you love what you do, you can easily fund your lifestyle by working part time. If you retire completely, you will be debt free and have your Social Security, tax-free money from your Personal Bank, money from the sale of your business, your 401(k) distributions, dividends from your stocks and possibly rental income, allowing you to continue to invest in equities. Social Security is like owning a big inflation-indexed bond delivering a stream of income that rises with inflation.

At the beginning of the annual Berkshire Hathaway meeting in 2018, Warren Buffett wanted to share an important lesson with its shareholders. I will summarize what he said: *"Let's look back to 1942* *when I bought my first stock and all the things that have happened since that time. We have had fourteen presidents, seven Republicans and seven Democrats. We had world wars, 9/11, Cuban missile crisis, and all kinds of terrible events that affected the market. But the best single thing you could have done on March 11, 1942 when I bought my first stock was to buy an index fund (Buffett specifically mentioned the S&P 500 index fund) and never ever look at another headline. Just like you would have bought a farm and let the tenant farmer run it for you and never sell it. If you had put in $10,000 in an index fund at that time and reinvested the dividends you would have $51 million today in 2018.*

If you took the same $10,000 and bought 300 ounces of gold, you would only have about $400,000 today. Gold does not produce anything, but businesses do. All you needed to do was to believe America would win the war and America would progress as it has ever since 1776. As America moves forward, American business moves forward. You didn't have to worry what stock to buy or what day to get in or out of the market or what the federal reserve would say. You just had to know that America works!"

Investment Vehicles for Pension Plans and IRAs

Once you are debt free and have maximized your contributions to your Personal Bank, I highly recommend that you take advantage of the various tax-deferred IRAs, pension and 401(k) plans that are available to you. In his recent book, *Unshakeable*, Tony Robbins spent a lot of time talking about how most companies that provide and manage 401(k) plans are ripping off the participants and owners of the plan. These plans are loaded with expensive mutual funds, excessive administrative expenses, and fat commissions to the brokers who sell the plan. In contrast, America's Best 401k is a company that offers only inexpensive index funds from firms such as Vanguard and dimensional fund advisors. Tom Zgainer, CEO of the company, charges only one fee with no markups or hidden costs. It is a full, bundled solution that eliminates brokers, commissions, and highly paid middlemen. He recommends investing with America's Best 401k to get the best returns at the lowest cost.

In addition to 401k plans, AB 401k also manages Cash Balance (CB) plans. When paired with a 401k, the CB plan allows for rapidly accelerated contributions while at the same time significantly reducing tax liability. These paired plans will generally work best when the dentist is older than forty with a staff mostly younger than the dentist. I recommend that you go to the website and use the company's free online Fee Checker tool at www.ShowMeTheFees.com. I have sent many of my clients to compare the fees at America's Best, and they have all moved their plans.

As an example, one of my dental clients who had about $1.4 million in her plan and added about $100,000 each year did a fee comparison. America's Best 401k total annual investment-related fees were 0.5%, compared to 1.73% in her original plan. If both plans got a 7% return over the next twenty years, the 1.23% difference in fees would have cost her $1.7 million in lost retirement savings. To look at this in another way, because of that 1.23% fee which would have resulted in a $1.7 million personal financial loss, she would have to work for another ten more years before retiring. Over a 30-year period the loss would be $4.93 million. How many more years do you have to work with a 3% advisor or actively managed fund fee? By eliminating the fees, it allows you to buy back the one thing that is limited in your life, which is your time on this planet. This is why it is essential that you compare your plans.

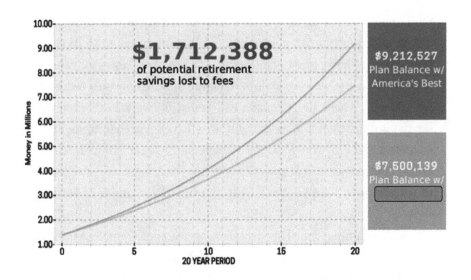

FIGURE 7

Estate Planning and Asset Protection Checklist

Over 30% of the endodontists I consult with do not have a will, power of attorney, or trust. Without these items, there is a great possibility that if something happens to you and your spouse, your drunken brother will take over all the money, spend it and throw your kids out on the street. Think about it. Without a revocable living trust, your estate will go into probate which makes all your assets public and is very expensive and emotionally draining to your heirs. It could take years before your estate is settled, thus depleting much of your estate's assets.

I was working with a thirty-four-year-old dentist who had a very nice practice, a little girl, and one more child on the way. I told him to go to his local attorney and get these estate planning documents drawn up. He said he would. Six months later, he was coming with his wife and team to one of my seminars in Seattle. During the flight, the plane had a landing gear issue and they thought they would have to make a crash landing in Seattle. Fortunately, they got the gear down and landed safely. At the meeting, I asked him, "Don't you feel better now that you have your asset protection plan in place?" He sheepishly said, "I will get those things done as soon as I get back."

Find a local attorney and get these things done now:

- Durable power of attorney for healthcare
- Durable power of attorney for finances
- Living will
- Standard will
- Revocable living trust
- Irrevocable trust

For a less expensive approach you can also go to LegalZoom and set up one for as little as $250 with the help of its attorneys. http://www.legalzoom.com/living-trusts/living-trusts-overview.html

Make sure to update beneficiaries on all your banking and investment accounts. The beneficiaries get first claim, and those listed on the will are secondary.

Recommended additional reading:

Dahle, James M., MD The White Coat Investor: A Doctor's Guide To Personal Finance And Investing. The White Coat Investor LLC.2014.

https://www.whitecoatinvestor.com/introduction-to-estate-planning/

https://www.thebalance.com/why-beneficiary-designations-override-your-will-2388824

Life Insurance.

In the past, I was a big fan of cheap term insurance, as compared to a standard, whole-life insurance policy. However, I have recently realized the power of having permanent whole-life insurance that can be modified to create your own Personal Bank as a high yield tax-free saving asset. This can be one of the best and safest places to save your money without risk while receiving consistent, predictable returns and can be a legacy to your family. Most insurance salesmen are unaware of this type of policy, so for more information on the Personal Bank go to personalbank4U.com.

Disability Insurance.

I recommend that you go to the Eagleston financial group to evaluate all your insurance needs, such as disability insurance.

Should you buy or rent a home? Bottom line:

Do not purchase a home until your student loans are all paid off and you have at least a 20% down payment. In 2019 the median home listing price in the US is nearly $280,000, according to Zillow, but that varies by state. The average American moves every 7 years. By then, only 12% of the home is paid off. Then they get a new mortgage, starting all over again at 100%. With a $280,000 mortgage they have paid $34,257 toward their mortgage and lost $90,569 to the bank in interest during those seven years. They also paid an additional 6% in sales commission ($16,800), $10,000 in home improvements, plus $4,000 in closing costs. The bottom line is that there was no increase in their net worth, and they will never ever get out of debt.

If they stay in the home and choose to pay back the original $280,000 loan at 4.9 % over the next 30 years, they will pay the $280,000 home price plus the $254,972 in interest, which equals $534,972 in after-tax money. I recommend that you never carry a mortgage larger than twice your gross income, and you should not spend more than 16% to 20% of your gross income on housing, including your mortgage payment, utilities, property tax, insurance and maintenance. Buy a home that is just large enough for your family and one that you can afford to pay off in seven to ten years. Make sure that you get a mortgage that has no penalty or fee for paying it off early. If you pay off the $280,000 home in seven years you would only need to pay $51,225 in interest and would save an additional $203,647 which would've gone to interest. Now you can use this money to invest in your retirement plan.

Remember: when buying a home over thirty years, most of the mortgage payments initially go to interest and very little goes to the principal (ownership) to pay off the home. For the first fifteen years it is just like renting, except you have all the additional property taxes, maintenance, and homeowner's insurance. Beyond that, in most cases you can't even write off the interest on your taxes because they are less than the standard deduction. You are much better off renting until you have a 20% down payment (to eliminate the need for private mortgage insurance) and can plan to pay off the house in seven to ten years. Focus all excess money on those payments and don't dilute your extra money by paying into children's college fund or into your retirement unless it's matched by your employer. Once debt-free, then you can invest in your children's college funding and other retirement plans. When you buy a home, you now have real estate in your portfolio and it becomes a form of forced savings, just like a long-term inflation-adjusted bond. And once paid off, that money which went to your mortgage payment now becomes like long-term dividends which can be invested more aggressively into the S&P 500 or total US stock market. Your paid-off home also becomes a safety net from which equity can be used in emergencies through home equity loans.

Unlike the dividends and interest from your investments, you don't have to pay taxes on inputted rent. This tax-free benefit is on top of the better-known tax breaks that home ownership enjoys, including the ability to take a tax deduction on the mortgage interest and property taxes, and to avoid capital gains tax on a big chunk of the profit when selling a home. In addition, when the market drops you just don't go out and sell your home like many investors do with their stocks.

The choice between buying a home and renting one is among the biggest financial decisions that many adults make. I would recommend renting if you do not plan to live in the house for longer than seven years. Here is a calculator that uses the most important costs associated with buying a house and computes the equivalent monthly rent. https://www.nytimes.com/interactive/2014/upshot/buy-rent-calculator.html

Get rid of private mortgage insurance (PMI).

If you did not have a 20% down payment when you purchased your house, you had to buy PMI, or private mortgage insurance. This is very expensive and can cost you up to 1% of the loan amount annually. A $400,000 house will require $4,000 a year in insurance payments, or $333 in monthly payments. In accordance with the Homeowners Protection Act of 1998, your lender must terminate PMI on the date your loan balance is scheduled to reach 78% of the original value of your home (in other words, when your equity reaches 22%, provided you are current on your mortgage payments). Call your lender and ask the lender to cancel your PMI when you have paid down the mortgage balance to 80% of the home's original appraised value. You might have to write your lender a cancellation letter of the PMI. Accelerate your payments as fast as you can to eliminate the PMI and, once you've done this, you'll have an additional $333 a month to pay off your home early. https://www.investopedia.com/mortgage/insurance/how-get-rid-pmi/

* * *

FINANCIAL MYTHS AND MISTAKES

Over the years, we have been imprinted with financial myths. Once we look closely at them, we realize how they are wrong and keep us from reaching our financial goals. Below, I will address a few of these beliefs and recommend you see them for what they are: myths. Also check out: https://www.whitecoatinvestor.com/stupid-doctor-tricks-biggest-financial-mistakes/

- **Myth 1: Good debt versus bad debt.** Some people say that your house or your business are good debt. But all debt is bad and sucks the life out of your financial world. We must

DR. ALBERT (ACE) GOERIG

remember that debt is the devil! Get rid of it as soon as possible. Becoming debt-free uncomplicates your life.

- **Myth 2: Pay yourself first and start saving for your retirement.** The problem with doing this is that you're only getting less than 1% return in your savings account when instead, you could use that money and get over 100% return right now by paying off debt, which is the fastest way to become wealthy.
- **Myth 3: Why pay off a 3% interest rate home loan when I can make 7% investing?** We must remember that we are really getting over 100% return by paying off our principal payment on our loans. And again, who says we are going to get 7% in the market? In some years, the market has dropped by 35%.
- **Myth 4: Buy the most expensive house you can afford.** This just keeps you in debt longer and adds many more expenses to your life. The more expensive the house, the more you will pay in property taxes, home maintenance, home upgrades, yard maintenance, and (if you live in such a neighborhood) community dues. You now must upgrade your lifestyle to keep up with the neighbors. Instead, buy someone *else's* dream house that fits your needs. You will save 20% versus building your own house and sidestep the headaches of construction. Dr. Doug Carlson says that home maintenance, property taxes, and upgrades average 2% of your home's value per year for a modest home. Thus, a $500K home will need $10,000 per year. Unfortunately, that peripheral cost of 2% will increase with a more expensive home. Often, you'll pay 3% for a $1.5 million home and over 4% for a $2M+ home. Yes, doctors can pay $80K and up each year for their "trophy" home. In Chapter 5, Dr. James M. Dahle, the author of *The White Coat Investor*, gives some good reasons why renting a home has its advantages during certain times in your career. Go to: https://www.whitecoatinvestor.com and type in "should I buy or rent?"

- **Myth 5: Emergency fund myth.** Some financial advisors recommend saving three to six months of living expenses in an emergency fund before you start paying off debt. The problem with this approach is that you never get around to paying off the debt, because it takes about two years to save up that amount, and meanwhile, many people take out the money for nonemergency items. You must begin to see debt as a tax, and automatically pay 10% to 20% of your monthly income toward your debt. Once your credit cards are paid off, you do have an emergency fund, you can get a line of credit, home equity loan or you can just stop paying those accelerated payments for one or two months.

- **Myth 6: The budgeting myth.** Again, many good financial advisors recommend you observe where you're spending your money and then budget so much each month, which allows you to set aside money to pay off debts. The problem is this give you a false sense of security and there is usually nothing left the end of the month. The secret of debt elimination is to automatically take 10% to 20% out of your bank account each month to pay off debt as if it were a tax. I can guarantee you that if you take 10% to 20% out each month and pay toward debt, you will be broke at the end of the month just like you are now, except you will be well on your way to becoming debt-free.

- **Myth 7: College funding myth.** Many people recommend that you start funding your child's education early, so that you have enough when they're ready for school. They might recommend 529 plans that are run by different states, which have high-load, actively managed funds. The returns are dismal. You also have less control over the money. It is better to focus on debt reduction and, when debt-free, you can easily fund your children's college education with cash. Create a high cash value personal bank for each of your children to fund college. Check out chapter 8 and personalbank4u.com.

- **Myth 8: The "more money" myth.** I've heard so many doctors say, "If I just had more money . . ." When I first began my coaching program, I showed endodontists how to make more money, but I forgot to teach them about getting out of debt. They just got into larger amounts of debt and are now trapped in their large homes and large high-stress lives. More money will not make you happy, but if you are focused on eliminating your debt, your life will become much more stress-free.

- **Myth 9: Life insurance as an investment.** This may be true with the standard whole-life insurance policies that are regularly sold, but with a highly modified high cash value whole-life insurance policy, it could be one of your best investments. Most insurance salesman are unaware of this type of policy, so for more information on the Personal Bank go to personalbank4U.com

- **Myth 10: Monthly payments are normal.** Our culture has taught us that we always need to be in debt. This makes a lot of money for many people in the banking and investment industries. So, stop paying them 100% interest.

- **Myth 11: Avoid-paying-taxes myth.** Endodontists lose money by trying different schemes to prevent paying taxes. You should want to pay more taxes than any other endodontists, because it indicates you are making more money than any other dentist. Rely on your CPA. A good CPA will keep you honest and make sure you don't give more to the government than you need to.

- **Myth 12: Financial advisor myth.** There is an old saying, "a broker will invest your money until you are broke." In the past, it was much more complicated to invest in the markets because people had to go to different brokerage houses and work through brokers. With the internet, it is easy to create an account online and find low-load index funds that will beat 96% of all the financial advisors because of the minimal 1% to 3% to manage your investments. Remember, a 1% advisory fee could cost you $1.5 million over twenty years if you had a $1.2 million 401k and you contributed $72,000 per year with an 8% return. For non-retirement money, use the free Schwab advisors and contribute each month into the S&P 500 index fund.

- **Myth 13: Myth of bi-weekly mortgage payments.** It is true that paying your mortgage twice a month will cause a 30-year mortgage to be paid off in about twenty-two years and save 25% of the interest. This strategy creates a false sense of security and keeps you from getting totally out of debt, including paying off the home, in five to seven years and saving 80% of the interest.

- **Myth 14: Don't pay off your house early because you can write off the interest rate on your taxes.** One of the biggest misconceptions that banks and accountants perpetuate is that you should not pay off your house early because you can write off the interest on your taxes. If we look at this closely, in 2018 an average American couple who pays $10,000 a year in interest has the choice of either take the standard deduction of $24,000 or to itemize their return and take the $10,000 tax write-off. When they itemize, they are unable to take the standard deduction of $24,000 and have an overall loss of $14,000.

Avoiding Financial Mistakes

Warren Buffett said; "the first rule of investment is, don't lose money. The second rule of investment is, never forget rule number one." The most important way to keep your wealth is to never make a big financial mistake. Big financial mistakes usually occur because of greed and ego. I have known numerous endodontists who have lost their entire portfolio in a get-rich-quick scheme. Such schemes range from real estate deals to limited partnerships; they can take the form of just about anything else that sounds too good to be true. Remember, *there is no free lunch*. When you have a systematic guide to get out of debt, increase your practice profitability, and conservatively invest in the US market, then you will become economically free in a fairly short time. Why take a risk on anything else? If you just stick with the boring *Dr. Ace's Financial Freedom* philosophy of investing, you'll never put your retirement money at risk. Here are some other financial mistakes that you should avoid.

- **Not stopping to find out what makes you happy.** The things that really make me happy are very simple and cost almost nothing. If I had known this earlier at the deepest level, I would not have needed to drive myself so hard to be successful. This is why the process of writing a new story is so important. Write down what you want your average day to look like. What are the things that make you happy? (Don't include shopping!) What are the happiest times you've enjoyed in your life? When you know who you are, it is easy to save money. Usually the simplest and least expensive things make you happy. Try to spend the least amount of money trying to figure out what makes you happy. Rent your way through the discovery process (for example, rent that lovely condo in the mountains rather than buy it). Most people live a life of high debt and stress because they spend money hoping it will make them happy. I guarantee that more money or things will not give you peace or happiness.

- **Allowing our ego to ruin our lives** by creating an unconscious compulsion to enhance one's identity through association with and purchase of expensive items, i.e. jewelry, exotic cars, and luxury homes. Yet rarely do these purchases satisfy the ego desires that make it feel different and special.

- **Lending money to friends and family.** If you lend money to friends or family, please realize there is a good possibility you will never be repaid. Often this has a negative impact on the relationship. If lending the money is meaningful to you, then consider simply giving it as a gift. Never cosign a loan; in most cases, you will end up paying the loan. A cosigner is a fool with a pen.

- **Falling for get-rich-quick schemes and scams.** Never get involved in any investment that you don't completely understand. With this guide, you do not have to take risk. You already have it made. When you are asked to invest in something new, just tell them that you only invest no-load S&P 500 or the US stock market, but thanks anyway. Check out: https://www.whitecoatinvestor.com/12-rules-to-help-you-avoid-getting-scammed/

- **Listening to investment financial advisors** who say they can beat the market. Only a fool would say they can beat the market, so just stick with no-load index funds that you can buy yourself.

- **Getting into a limited partnership.** You lose control as a limited partner and are the last to be paid. Stay away from any investment or thing that you do not understand thoroughly or do not have personal control of decisions over.

- **Living in a high-cost, high-congestion and high-tax area.** If you to work and live in a large city like San Francisco or New York City where homes can be two to three times more expensive, you will find that traffic is terrible and there are high state and city taxes can delay your becoming debt-free and financially free. Think about moving to a tax-free state such as Texas, Florida, Wyoming, Washington, Alaska, New Hampshire, South Dakota, Tennessee or Nevada. Live in a smaller, less expensive and hectic community, and be able to buy a nicer and bigger home that you can pay off in five to seven years.

- **Buying too big a house.** Consider what you really need. Buying a bigger house than you need wastes money monthly. The cost of your home should not exceed two times your gross salary.

- **Buying a vacation home or large boat that you rarely use.** If this adds meaning to your life and you use it often, like more than sixty days a year, then it is worth the investment. That is, until it no longer adds meaning to your life—and at that time, you can sell it. It is not a bad idea for some properties like vacation homes or boats to be shared with other owners to dilute the expenses.

- **Buying timeshares.** Never buy them. You have a greater selection and a lot less price if you go to vacation rental by owner (VRBO.com).
- **Buying annuities.** Never buy them.
- **Starting another business** before you start making your own practice successful. A well-run dental practice can be one of the most successful businesses on this planet. Maintain your focus and start having fun again in your practice.
- **Marry the right person the first time.** Stay away from spenders. Find someone who is conservative in their spending habits and has financial goals.
- **Not getting a prenuptial agreement if you have assets.** Get your spouse (male or female) to sign on the dotted line before you say, "I do."
- **Having too many "successful" marriages.** Before divorcing, try to reinvent your relationship and work through a counselor to see if you can make the relationship work. If there is no possibility of working it out, then you both deserve your freedom. There's often a lot of anger and trying to "get even" in the divorce process. I recommend that you offer your spouse a generous settlement and treat them with kindness and respect. Always try to maintain strong relationships with your children; never put down your partner. If your spouse wants more and does not accept your generous offer, then tell your attorney that his or her job is simply to get you in front of the judge and no longer communicate with your spouse's attorney. This will save both of you a lot money in attorney fees. Judges are normally fair in their settlements. If you continue to marry the same type of person (alcoholic, codependent, crazy), then this is the time for some personal growth and counseling.

Chapter 7

HOW THE MARKETS WORK AND
THE BEST INVESTMENT OPTIONS

DANIEL SOLIN HAS WRITTEN MANY must-read investment books. In two of these books, *The Smartest Money Book You'll Ever Read* and *The Smartest Investment Book You'll Ever Read,* he summarized the key points about investing:

- It is not complicated.
- No one has a clue about where the market is headed.
- Stay away from individual stocks that expose you to higher risk without higher expected returns.
- Stay away from actively managed mutual funds (brokers) that increase your fees, cost, and reduce your expected return.
- Never use the services of a broker or advisor who claims to be able to beat the market.
- Determine your asset allocation and invest in low-cost index funds such as the S&P 500 (passively managed) index fund, which will beat 96% of all financial advisors and brokers. There are other, more conservative, investments listed below.

- The free-market system works. Stock prices are random and efficient. There is no mispricing. Always stay in the market.
- Don't listen to the news (turn off the noise).

Understanding the Risks of the Market

Very few people understand the stock market, and no one can accurately predict changes in the market. Jack Bogle, the founder of Vanguard group, says, *"Nobody knows nothing about the market."* Many brokers tell you to buy a stock when it is high and tell you not to buy when it drops. But common sense would tell us the best time to buy stocks is when they're low. Even worse, some brokers tell you to get out of the market when it drops. When we invest in equities (stocks) we are always on shifting sands; we are always taking a risk. And when we invest, we should not invest in actively managed mutual funds but stay with low-cost passively managed index funds such as the S&P 500, which has consistently done better than 96% of all funds on the market.

When you have a guide for obtaining financial freedom that is safe and predictable, why take a risk? Anyone who can work and save money has it made; financial freedom is yours for the taking. Your ability to earn money and pay off debt is the most important thing in developing economic abundance. Your income is like a large inflation-protected bond that allows you to put a greater amount of your investment portfolio into stocks. Investments are for added income for your retirement, not to make you rich. Your earnings from your job will make you rich if you live within your means and consistently save or store part of them. Individuals who do this now work two to three days a week and continue to do something they really enjoy that brings in money. They will never, ever use up the money they've set aside for retirement.

The Big Scam

According to *Forbes* ("Why the Average Investor's Return Is So Low," by Sean Hanlon, April 24, 2014), over a ten-year period (2004 to 2013), the S&P 500 has averaged 7.4% return. The reason average investors have realized only a 2.6% return during that same time is because they are in actively managed funds, which constantly trade in and out of the market, and the investors pay high fees in commissions, trading fees and taxes to their brokers. Many brokers buy and sell securities within the funds repeatedly, to try to improve their performance. This boosts transaction cost and taxes. These costs are buried in your management fees, which compensate the fund manager. These can cost you up to 3% to 4% annually. Many fund managers keep money in cash, so they can time the market. This is called *cash drag* and gives you a zero performance on that money, compared with what you could've gotten in an index fund.

Most individual investors rely upon money managers, advisors and brokers who engage in hyperactive trading to try to beat the market by picking winners and timing the market. This is a losing strategy. In most cases, investors would be better off consistently investing in index funds like the S&P 500. Jack Bogle, founder of the Vanguard group, believes in index funds and says actively managed funds are a big scam. When you invest in loaded, actively managed mutual funds, you put up 100% of the capital and take 100% of the risk, and if you make money, they take up to 70% or more of the upside in fees. And if you lose money, they still get paid. They are charging you 10 to 30 times what it would cost for you to buy a low-cost index fund that would match the market and beat 96% of the mutual funds. Because fees are the enemy of the individual investor, we need to stay away from financial advisors and brokers who work on commission and thus put us into actively managed funds.

Here is an example from one of my clients who had more

than $1.6 million that was managed by a large brokerage firm. Over a six-year period, his portfolio would have built *$863,881 more in assets* if it had been placed into a Schwab S&P 500 fund. Compare your portfolio to the S&P 500, and see how you do. Go to Doctorace.com for more videos and audios, and download and fill out the Excel comparison sheet seen below.

Remember, the S&P 500 fund performs better than 96% of all other managed funds, and I have yet to see any of my clients whose portfolio has done better than the S&P 500 index fund. In most cases, they have lost significant amounts of money when they let the experts invest.

	Schwab S&P 500 mutual fund index	brokerage **taxable** account		Loss	brokerage **401K** account		Loss
Ticker sym	SWPPX						
Fees	0.03%		1%		$0		
Cost/ 1M$	$300		$10,000		$10,000		
Stocks/Bonds	100%/0		100%/0		100%/0		
Invested		Opening balance			Opening balance		
2018	-4.40%	$455,347	-7.00%	($11,839)	$1,300,000	-1.00%	$44,200
2017	21.80%	$406,560	12.00%	($39,843)	$1,276,633	9.50%	($157,026)
2016	12.0%	$321,784	6.5%	($17,698)	$1,099,332	1.27%	($117,958)
2015	1.4%	$316,367	-2.3%	($11,706)	$1,262,352	-2.28%	($46,455)
2014	13.7%	$302,687	4.5%	($27,847)	$1,322,966	6.29%	($98,032)
2013	32.4%	$356,161	7.9%	($87,259)	$1,186,118	11.37%	($249,441)
2012	16.0%	$272,222	12.1%	($10,617)			$0
			Loss	($206,809)		Loss	($624,711)
						Total Loss	($831,520)

	Schwab S&P 500 mutual fund index	Brokerage taxable account Opening balance each year	Added money that year	Total invested	Your brokarage return that year	Loss (red) Gain (black)
Ticker sym	SWPPX					
Fees	0.03%				1%	
Cost/ 1M$	$300				$10,000	
Stocks/Bonds	100%/0				100%/0	
Invested		Opening balance	Added money			
2018	-4.40%			$0	#DIV/0!	#DIV/0!
2017	21.80%			$0	#DIV/0!	#DIV/0!
2016	12.0%			$0	#DIV/0!	#DIV/0!
2015	1.4%			$0	#DIV/0!	#DIV/0!
2014	13.7%			$0	#DIV/0!	#DIV/0!
2013	32.4%			$0	#DIV/0!	#DIV/0!
2012	16.0%			$0	#DIV/0!	#DIV/0!
2011	2.1%			$0	#DIV/0!	#DIV/0!
2010	15%			$0	#DIV/0!	#DIV/0!
2009	26.30%			$0	#DIV/0!	#DIV/0!
					Total Loss/gain	#DIV/0!

Another must-read book is Anthony Robbins' *Unshakeable*. He writes about the two enemies of the investor: fear and fees. Most money is lost in the market because of these two factors. If you are an investor and put your money in an actively managed mutual fund, you will pay 3.17% of the non-taxable account toward fees (4.17% if it's a taxable account). Look at the chart below to see what this 3% difference in fees would cost you over 20, 30, or 40 years if the S&P 500 average 7% growth. You would have two to three times more earnings.

	4% growth	7% growth	Earnings Difference
20 years	$191,996	$425,948	2.2x
30 years	$504,544	$1,300,631	2.6x
40 years	$1,058,851	$3,220,187	3.1x

The second greatest enemy of the investor is fear. Getting out of the market when it starts to drop is a mistake. This is the time you need to *buy*. You have a good portfolio of index funds you should always stay in, because they will always rebound. From 1997 to 2016, the S&P 500 index returned 7.7%. If you were out of the market during the top ten days, your return would've dropped to 4%; the top 20 days, your return would've been 1.6%; and if you were out of the market the top 40 days, your return would've been a *negative* 2.4%. The message is clear: when the market drops, *do not* get out of the market, and continually keep buying more index funds like the S&P 500 as it drops. The free-market system works. Stock prices are random and efficient. There is no mispricing. Always stay in the market.

Understanding Index Funds

Many *individual* stocks are not safe on a long-term basis, which is why we focus on *index funds* that represent the whole United States market and thus spread the risk across many securities. Warren Buffett, the legendary investor and business magnate, believes in the American economy and has said that he would invest the money he leaves to his children in a Vanguard S&P 500 fund. An index fund is a passively managed mutual fund made up of the securities (stocks or bonds) in a stock index in the proportions the index devises. The most followed stock-market indexes are the Dow Jones industrial average (DJIA) and the Standard and Poor's 500 (S&P 500). The DJIA is based on 30 major companies; the S&P 500 has 500 companies; the NASDAQ has 3900 listings, and the Wilshire 5000 total market index is the broadest index for the US stock market.

The advantages of investing in index funds are as follows:

- Passive investing (avoids excessive fees, commissions and taxes)
- Diversification spreads risk across many securities
- Low management fees
- Income from dividend returns
- Predictable risk (lower than individual securities)
- Easy to purchase by yourself without paying brokerage fees
- Performance better than 96% of actively managed funds

Actively Managed Funds Compared to Index (Passively Managed) Funds

In actively managed funds, the financial advisor or broker tries to beat the market by timing the market and selecting winning stocks. This results in the client's money moving into and out of the market numerous times and leads to a high commission for the financial advisor and expenses to the investor through trading costs, short-term capital gains tax, and cash drag (money held out of the market and not being invested). These expenses significantly reduce your overall return, and most of these funds never beat the average S&P 500 index fund. This 3% to 4% (400 basis points) expense results in a 50% to 70% loss in the return of your investments over time. This is why fees are so important. You can get an S&P 500 index fund for as little as 0.03% (3 basis points), which mirrors the components of a market index and has no other costs.

Corrections in the Market

There are always corrections in the market, and you must welcome them as a great opportunity to buy more index funds on sale. This is a paradigm shift, and we must develop an attitude of excitement, not fear, when the market drops, because that's when stocks are on sale. Below is a chart of the average historical corrections of the market from 1900 to 2015.

Average Historical Corrections of the Market				
	Regular Decline (5% or more)	Modest Correction (10% or more)	Serious Correction (15% or more	Bear Market (20% or more)
Frequency	3 times/year	1 times/year	Every 2 years	Every 3 years
Average loss before drop ends	11%	19%	27%	35%
Average duration	40 days	109 days	217 days	364 days

In his recent book *Unshakeable*, Tony Robbins states that, over the past 70 years, there have only been 14 bear markets, averaging one every five years, lasting an average of one year and ranging from 45 days to nearly two years. He says that what you need to know is that bear markets don't last and are always followed by a bull market during the next 12 months. From March 9, 2009, the S&P 500 index surged by 69.5% over the next 12 months.

Since 2009, we have not had a bear market (20% or more drop) and only one 17% drop in 2010 and an 18% drop in 2011. Since then, we have had only 10 corrections in the S&P 500 that were greater than 10%. 2018 was a very volatile year, with drops of 7%, 11% and 19.7%. This is probably because of the ending of the Federal Reserve's policy of quantitative easing from 2009 to 2014 and low interest rates, forcing more investors into the market. 2018 was a great year to test your risk tolerance and an excellent year to buy stocks at the bottom. Even though there were significant corrections, the overall loss that year was a -4.4%. Remember, it becomes a loss only if you sell.

Your Personal Bank and the stock market is just a place to store your money for better long-term returns for retirement. Long-term investing in Index funds like the S&P 500 can give you 3 to 4 times the return, compared to a less-risky bond portfolio. When you are debt free, it becomes easier to invest into stocks like the S&P 500. For most investors, this is all we need to do, and we can quit worrying about the market.

Dealing with Your Investment Emotions

As humans, we are wired with a fight-or-flight emotional base. Our emotions make life worth living, but uncontrolled emotions while investing can be deadly. I highly recommend that you read Jason Zweig's book entitled *Your Money and Your Brain: How the New Science of Neuroeconomics Can Help Make You Rich.* It will help you understand your emotions during investing. If you are unable to understand or cannot discipline and control your emotions when there is a 10%, 20% or even 40% drop in the market, then you should place your money in your Personal Bank and not worry about the market. Great investors spend little time watching the market but do have a simple and safe game plan that they stick with. They have patience, available cash and courage, and they know market history well enough to wait for the drops in the market that always come. Once you understand the history of the market, then you respond with logic instead of a knee-jerk reaction from your fear. Stop listening to the financial (all) news throughout the year. Some investors continue to contribute monthly, automatically, to the S&P 500 or US total stock market index fund in your Schwab account through dollar-cost averaging (DCA). Others put their money in their Personal Bank and money-market account, wait for a greater-than 10% drop in the market, and buy more, using their discretionary income if the market drops further. That's it, you're done. Remember: Being debt free and having a paid-off home and business, cash value in a Personal Bank and a steady income puts 80% to 90% of your net worth in inflation-adjusted, secure bond-like assets. This allows the 10% to 20% of your net worth to be invested in the S&P 500 without worry, knowing you are in it for the long game. It is that simple.

What Do You Do When the Market Tanks?

When the stock market drops and we see our portfolio being reduced, our fight-or-flight emotions are stimulated. Long-term investors get excited rather than depressed because they realize the opportunities they have been given by this drop. Below is a step-by-step approach for you to remember during downturns in the market.

1. Understand and control your emotions. You need to switch your emotions to excitement because you are now able to use your built-up cash in your money-market account to buy the S&P 500 or dividend-paying stocks *on sale*. Warren Buffett says that opportunities of a 15% to 30% bear-market drop rarely occur, and when they do, you need to buy as much of the good companies or S&P 500 as you can while they are on sale.

2. Remember that you have seen this picture before and you know how it ends, so **never sell**, only **buy** when the market drops.

3. Warren Buffett said if you can detach yourself from the crowd and become greedy while others

are fearful, you can become very rich, and you don't have to be smart. It does not take brains; it takes temperament.

4. Remind yourself that you are debt free, that you have a constant source of income and that these great opportunities occur only a few times in your life.

5. Start rounding up more cash and hope it drops further for even greater opportunities.

6. Wonder what Warren Buffett is thinking (he is very happy).

7. Get back to loving your life.

Stop listening to all the financial advice on television. This is just noise. Once you are debt free and have a highly profitable, effortless and fun business, you never have to worry about money again. Saving money in your Personal Bank and investing in index funds when there are drops in the market is the most efficient way to save your money and become rich slowly. You do not care about the market. Warren Buffett said if the stock market closed down for five years, it would not make a difference in his decision to invest. Remember to always stay in the market, and understand that drops in the market are opportunities to buy.

Steps to Individual Investing on Your Own

When you learn to invest on your own, you become the chess player instead of the chess piece. With the internet, investing in the market on your own is very simple. You first need to open a brokerage account with a well-known investment company that provides excellent service with low fees and a wide range of low-cost index funds. I believe that both Vanguard and Schwab are excellent companies. **So, do it *today*.** I have accounts with both Vanguard and Schwab, but I find that Schwab is more customer oriented. It is open 24 hours a day, seven days a week and has excellent representatives and brokers. Schwab also requires no dollar minimums to open an account, the lowest expense ratios, and when you buy its mutual funds and index ETFs (exchange-traded funds), there are no trading costs, compared to other companies. All other trades are only $4.95 a trade.

All representatives and brokers from Schwab and Vanguard are salaried; they do not work on commission, so their advice focuses on your best interests. The company also has agents located in most cities. These local Schwab brokers can help you through the process, or you may go online and have an account set up within 30 minutes. Because you are transferring your accounts to them, ask to get 20 free trades. Once you set up an account, then you can start putting money into specific mutual funds or follow some of the strategies that I will mention below. I also recommend becoming familiar with the Yahoo Finance and Morningstar websites to help you best understand the past performance of different funds.

Investment Strategies

If you follow this guide, get out of debt and make more money, you will never have to worry about money. Most individuals could be totally debt free in seven to ten years. Just don't do stupid things with money. Now, stop worrying. In chapter 8 are investment options to put your mind at ease, knowing you are getting the best return on your investments within your risk tolerance without paying high fees and commissions. *Pick the options that work best for you and your risk tolerance, and then you're done. It's that simple*.

The best investment strategies are always simple and easy to understand. Brokers want to sell you complex investments that you don't understand so they can charge high fees and commissions, which often results in lower returns to you as the investor. Once you understand your risk tolerance and how the market works over time, then select the options that fit your comfort zone and your desired rate of return. Remind yourself that you are a long-term investor, and then stay in the market during corrections. When the market drops, you should be elated because stocks are on sale, and this is the time to buy and add to your portfolio. But before you invest, you should first understand your asset allocation and risk tolerance.

Investment Strategies Need to Change with the Times

The way we invest today is dramatically different than it was forty years ago. We can now go online, open a brokerage account with Schwab or Vanguard, and buy low-cost index funds that match the market and do better than 96% of all actively managed funds. In 1980, mortgage interest rates reached an all-time high of 18.4%, and you could buy a 14%, non-callable, 30-year, AAA-rated, tax-free municipal bond. That was when you would buy only bonds. In early 2000, you could buy 10-year, AAA-rated, tax-free municipal bonds at 5% or 6% with a guaranteed after-tax yield of 8% to 9%. Back then, there was no need to risk your money in the stock market.

Over the past 15 years, interest rates have decreased to almost 0%. A 10-year treasury note or CD is getting only about a 2.5% return, and this does not even keep up with inflation. This is a tragedy for those who are retired, living on a fixed income, and relying on the interest from their investments. Fifteen years ago, they were getting around a 5% return in their bank saving accounts, and now they are getting less than 1%. If you are relying upon the interest from bonds to live on in your retirement, you may run out of money and may have to add more stock index funds to your portfolio.

The more averse you are to risk, the more of your portfolio should be in in your Personal Bank with an average tax-free return of around 5% which is like a before tax return of around 8% to 9%. When you are buying stock index funds such as the S&P 500 and the total US stock index fund, you are buying United States businesses that, over time, will return three to four times what bond funds will earn. Many of these US businesses do have international holdings. You must see stock index funds investments as a savings account and stay in for the long term. Stock index funds are less risky the longer you hold them, while the longer the maturity of bonds, the riskier they become. But if you are one who gets upset with price fluctuations in the stock market, then you should not own stocks. Put more of your money into your Personal Bank and any extra into high-yielding bank CDs, Schwab money market accounts or short-term two- to five-year US treasury bonds.

Remember, even if we get a 10% return with our stock (S&P 500) portfolio, your real return would be about 7% once adjusted to 3% inflation. A portfolio of 50% stocks and 50% bonds has an expected return of only 6%, and, after adjusting for inflation of 3%, you are now down to a return of 3%. That is why we need to eliminate the 1% fee you pay your advisor and the 2% fee for the mutual fund, which could leave us with 0% return. If you invested in bonds returning only about 2%, you would have a negative return. Because of the current historical low interest rates, bonds return only about 2%.

Remember your history

Warren Buffett likes to quote Mark Twain when he supposedly said, "History doesn't repeat itself, but it often rhymes." Michael Alexander wrote a book entitled *Stock Cycles*. He reviews the markets over 200 years of American history until the year 2000. During that time, we have had seven long-term bear and seven long-term bull markets. The total average real return in a long-term bull market was 13.2%, while the average return in a long-term bear market was 0.3%. For example, from 1966 to 1982, the total real return was a -1.5%. But from 1982 to 2000, the average total real return of the market was 14.8%. Alexander then went on to predict that, starting in 2000, there would be a long-term bear market. In March 2013, the price of the Standard & Poor's (S&P) 500 was 1527, the same price as it was in March 2000, resulting in no growth of the stock, which is why those 13 years are called "the lost decade." Those who had their money in a Personal Bank were getting a consistent 4% to 6% return each year during that lost decade and never worried what the market was doing. That time period was a very turbulent time for investors, but an exceptionally great time for those understood the phrase by Warren Buffett, who once said that as an investor, it is wise to *be fearful when others are greedy and greedy when others are fearful.* Today many investors think the market is reaching its peak, which may be one reason why Warren Buffett, as of 2019, has more than $112 billion in cash equivalents. It has been more than 10 years since we have had a bear market, and, like Warren, I am keeping a majority of my powder dry. After funding my Personal Bank, I will automatically put money into my Schwab account monthly, keeping more money in liquid assets such as US treasuries and money-market accounts that are returning more than 2%. The cash value in my Personal Bank and the liquid assets in my treasury and money-market accounts will allow me to take advantage of possible opportunities if the market drops 10% to 35% over the next one to three years. Remember, no one can predict the market, so, on this matter, you must make your own decision.

Chapter 8

INVESTMENT OPTIONS BASED ON RISK

Option 1a: Pay off all debt. Safe! No Risk! Highest Tax-Free Return!!!

Paying off debt is mandatory *before* investing and is like getting the highest-grade inflation-protected bond with a guaranteed interest rate of more than 100%, risk-free. Set up an automatic payment each month toward the principal of your next debt in your debt-elimination payments.

Option 1b: Create Your Own Personal Bank. Safe! No Risk! Tax-Free Return!

Creating your own Personal Bank comes from the concept of infinite banking by Nelson Nash in the 1980s. It has also been known as Private Family Bank, Bank on Yourself, Infinite Banking or High Cash Value Life Insurance. It uses a specially designed high cash value whole life insurance policy that maximizes cash value in the policy enabling you to store your money safely while receiving a tax-free guaranteed 4% to 5% return. Plus, it provides a death benefit for your family. Like a savings account, the cash value in the policy can be used and accessed at any time for any reason. This option is for everyone but especially for those who are fearful of the risks and the volatility of the stock market. The main purpose of your own Personal Bank is to provide a place to save money while receiving a high tax-free yield, build wealth and create a consistent stream of income to invest and to use for retirement. When debt free, you need a place to keep your wealth tax free and never have to borrow from a bank again because now you can borrow from your own Personal Bank.

Creating your own Personal Bank would entail working with a life insurance agent who meets specific criteria. This agent must know how to design a whole life insurance policy that maximizes cash value and satisfies the IRS's non-MEC requirements. They should also work with the top four mutual insurance companies, which are Mass Mutual, Guardian, New York Life, and Northwestern mutual. These 4 major mutual companies all have a guaranteed rate of 4% and pay a surplus in addition. The guaranteed rate plus the surplus equates to the total dividend rate. The top 4 companies paid rates between 5.00% - 6.40% for 2019. These companies have always paid a dividend for the 160+ years they've been around.

Lafayette Life insurance company is another highly rated mutual company that is used by many agents who provide high cash value whole life insurance policies. If you work with these agents, make sure that the policy is designed so no more than 10% of premiums go to the base death benefit and the rest is directed toward cash value.

These are "mutually owned" life insurance companies that enable you to participate in the company's profits and dividends at the end of the year. Correctly designed policies maximize your cash accumulation by putting 10% of your premium toward death benefits and 90% toward cash value and small term rider. This reduces an agent's commission by 70% to 90%. The policy's primary use is to hold and build cash in a guaranteed tax-deferred 4% to 5% return safe environment to be used for future investments with the death benefit being secondary. The life insurance policy gives you more safety, liquidity, flexibility and control of your money than any savings vehicle or retirement plan you will own. This is why it has been used by major banks, Fortune 500 Companies, and the wealthy for more than a century and is often their # 1 Asset.

The cash value in the policy grows tax free and all money borrowed from the policy is tax-free. You earn a guaranteed tax free 4% to 5% each year including dividends. This is what the average stock investor earns each year except the returns from your Personal Bank are tax free. Within the first year, more than 85% of the premiums are now available as cash value. On average, after 3 to 4 years all your premiums paid are available in cash value. Money can be retrieved from your account for any reason through a loan process without any application or approval by using your cash value as collateral. You borrow from the company's general fund at a 5% interest rate. Because you borrow the money from the insurance company's general fund all cash value in your policy continues to grow at around 5%, which is as good as a free loan.

As an example, if you have $100,000 in cash value, you can borrow up to $100,000 from the company's general fund using your cash value as collateral. This leaves your cash value intact to continue to earn your guaranteed 5% return on the $100,000. Over the next 10 years you will have paid $27,268 in loan interest back to the insurance company. During that same 10 years your $100,000 in your cash value has earned $64,701 in interest and dividends! In fact, the growth of your cash value has covered the $27,268 of loan interest and has given you a $37,433 profit. Even though the 5% interest is the same on the growth and the loan, you are always earning the 5% interest and dividends on an ever-increasing cash value balance while the 5% you are paying on the loan is on a decreasing loan balance. Because you are borrowing the money and not withdrawing the money from your cash value, there are no taxes on the capital gains. During your retirement years, you can borrow money each year from your cash value tax-free and never pay it back. The interest and money you borrowed will be deducted from your death benefits.

When borrowing money from your policy, understand that there is a difference between non-direct recognition and direct recognition insurance companies. When you borrow from a non-direct recognition company, they do not recognize that you borrowed money from your cash value and will continue to credit you the same dividends and interest as if you never took out a loan. The loan interest on the borrowed money goes to the insurance company. The death benefit and cash value will be reduced by the loan payment until the loan is paid back. You will still earn their yearly dividend rate on the total cash value and when the loan is paid back, the death benefits and cash value are completely restored as if you never had a loan. Mass Mutual insurance is an example of a non-direct recognition company.

With a direct recognition company such as Guardian, you will receive their dividend rate on all money still in cash value. You will also receive a slightly different dividend on the money that is outstanding in policy loans, which closely matches whatever the loan interest rate. With some direct recognition insurance companies, the dividend paid on the loan portion can be significantly lower than your loan interest rate. This is usually true with smaller companies, so always check with the agent to determine the true historical dividend paid on borrowed money. The main take away is that direct recognition companies still pay a dividend on borrowed money but at different rates. Guardian insurance company is a direct recognition company and currently pays a slightly higher dividend on borrowed money. Guardian also has an option to change your policy from a direct recognition to a non-direct recognition at year 10.

The question is how much do you want to save? This is a high-powered savings program with a death benefit. You must see the premiums not as bills but deposits into your cash value savings account. So how big do you want your cash value (savings) to grow over time? The cash value is a combination of the premiums you pay and the interest and dividends that the policy earns each year. This creates an exponential growth curve.

Most life insurance policies are sold on how cheaply they can provide a death benefit. They say that you should buy term insurance and invest the difference. The problem is very few people invest the difference and less than 2% of term policies claims are paid which means all that money put into term insurance is lost. With a high cash value whole life insurance policy we want to know how much premium we can put into the policy's cash value rather than into death benefit costs. The death benefit is a bonus. The policy is designed to optimize cash value accumulation and then we will determine how much death benefit we will buy.

Because the policy is designed to increase the cash value, they add a paid-up addition (PUA) rider which provides small amounts of death benefits through term insurance that enable them to significantly increase the cash value in a much higher ratio than the base policy can. The PUA rider allows for a large cash value in your policy. The insurance companies require that at least 10% of the premiums go into life insurance (death benefit). So, 10% of your premiums go to base whole life policy and 90% goes to PUA's for cash value and a small term policy rider while making up 100% of your Personal Bank premium. Remember that the cash value grows tax free and can be accessed tax-free. That is why the tax-free 5% you are getting from your whole life insurance policy is like an 8% return in the market where you must pay capital gains taxes on your non-IRA accounts or personal income tax on withdrawals from your 401(k) plan. The comparable return may even be 9% to 10% in your Personal Bank when you consider the

2% to 4% loss in advisory or mutual fund fees and the money lost buying term insurance.

In designing the plan, your agent must be knowledgeable about how much cash is built into the policy to ensure the policy is not classified as a modified endowment contract (MEC) based on the IRS Seven Pay rule. In 1988 the tax law changed because certain insurance policies funded cash value too rapidly and were classified as a modified endowment contract. The IRS eliminated the use of such policies as short-term tax-free savings vehicles by imposing stiff penalties. The IRS created the Seven Pay Test rule were the IRS limits the total amount you can pay into a policy in any consecutive seven years of its existence. This amount is compared to the sum of the net level premiums that could have been paid on a guaranteed seven-year pay whole life policy providing the same death benefits. If you tried to put too many premium dollars in the cash value compared to the policy's death benefit you have crossed the dreaded MEC line. To satisfy the MEC rule the death benefit is raised through a cheap term insurance rider allowing greater cash value in the policy.

Total Payments

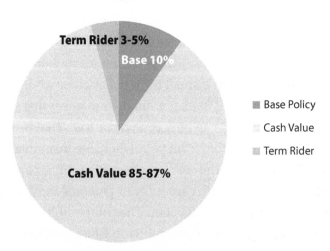

Each policy needs to be custom designed to meet each person's individual long-term financial goals, your current financial needs, your current cash flow, your current savings, and your legacy needs.

You can also borrow money for your retirement out of these policies and not pay back the loans. The Personal Bank is more like a defined benefit plan, most often known as a pension, because it promises you a set payout when you retire. Because of costs, most employers have eliminated defined benefit plans and replaced them with defined contribution plans, like a 401(k) or 403(b). These plans place the burden of investing on the employee with no guarantee of investment returns or specific benefits when they retire. Your Personal Bank has many more advantages over a regular 401(k) plan. There are no restrictions like you find in qualified retirement plans such as minimum distributions, restrictions and penalties on withdrawal before age 59, and all distributions are taxed at your personal tax rate. Your Personal Bank also allows you to make larger contributions than most traditional qualified plans. Your investment growth is tax deferred; you can access your funds tax free, and you have a death benefit with all inheritance income going tax free to your heirs.

The Personal Bank becomes your legacy and you can create participating whole life policies on yourself, your children and your grandchildren and be the owner of each policy. As these children get older, the policies' cash value can be used to buy their first car, help with their college education, weddings and their new business. The children re-pay these loans back to your bank.

The Personal Bank is the ideal saving vehicle for your children's education. In contrast, if your child needs to take out a private loan, they will have to fill out a loan application. The application has all the income and credit score requirements of any regular bank loan. If the student has no credit history, a co-signer may be required. The student or co-signer's FICO score determines the loan's interest rate. The co-signer is obligated for the loan's repayment. Repayment consistency affects the co-signer's FICO score. Compare this to a Personal Bank student loan application where there is no application process. You simply submit the loan amount to the insurance company and receive the money in about 5 business days.

Comparing a normal student loan repayment plan, the student must begin repaying most federal student loans right after s/he leave college or drop below half-time enrollment, plus loans start repayment once the loan is fully disbursed (paid out). That can even be while the student is still in school. A Personal Bank student loan, on the other hand, can be paid back however and whenever you, the policy owner, choose.

Let's compare a 529 plan to using a Personal Bank. Withdrawals from a 529 plan are tax-free to the extent your child (or other account beneficiary) incurs Qualified Higher Education Expenses (QHEE) during the year. If you withdraw more than the QHEE, the excess is a non-qualified distribution. Whoever receives this non- qualified money will have to report taxable income and pay a 10% federal penalty tax on the earnings portion of the non-qualified distribution. You CANNOT include the following expenses: insurance, sports or club activity fees, and many other types of fees that may be charged to your students but are not required as a condition of enrollment. The expenses for a computer may not be included unless the institution requires that students have their own computers. Other costs that may not be included are transportation costs (like bringing junior home for the holidays), repayment of student loans and room and board costs in excess of the amount the school includes in its "cost of attendance" figures for federal financial aid purposes.

529 plan Contributions cannot exceed the amount necessary to provide for the qualified education expenses of the beneficiary. Be aware that there may be gift tax consequences if your contributions, plus any other gifts, to a particular beneficiary exceed $14,000 during the year. A 529 account owned by a parent for a dependent

student is reported on the federal financial aid application (FAFSA) as a parental asset. Any money remaining in a 529 account after education expenses are withdrawn is subject to standard qualified plan withdrawal and taxation rules. And, lest we forget, 529 plans are invested in mutual funds in the stock and bond markets where values fluctuate and could be down when needed.

When the Personal Bank is used for education expenses, the policy owner alone decides what the money can be used for. There is no such thing as a non-qualified distribution. There are no penalties under any circumstances. There are no regulatory limits on, or tax consequences to, how much you put into a Personal Bank for funding a child's education. While it's true that, once a policy is underwritten, it is limited to that maximum funding level. However, you can start additional policies to add any amount you want to your savings. Money saved in a Personal Bank is not reported on applications for college financial aid. Money remaining in a Personal Bank policy after education expenses have been withdrawn, grows tax-free, can be taken out tax-free, and will pass on to the beneficiary tax-free.

Ownership of the policy can also be transferred to the student. Policy cash value always goes up, so there's no fear of market volatility when the money is needed. It's much simpler, more flexible, and less risky to pay for a child's or grandchild's education through a Personal Bank policy loan than through any typical student loan. Plus, it offers a powerful additional benefit that no student loan offers, which is the death benefit on the life of the person paying into the policy. The student can be designated as the beneficiary. A trust can be designated to control responsible use of the money. The main point here is, if you live and can fully fund the Personal Bank to pay for the child's education, it's paid for. If you die before you're able to save up enough, the death benefit will fund the child's education. This is better than any other savings plan.

It can get even better. Once the student's education is

complete and they have a job, the policy owner can make them a life-changing offer. If the child makes loan payments and pays off the policy loan balance over time, the parent or grandparent can agree to transfer policy ownership to the child at that time. This will not only transfer control of the policy's cash value to the child, but teaches them the value of saving, the importance of getting out of debt, conservative safe investing, and help them implement a forced savings plan for their retirement. It provides them with a wealth-building system they can continue to profit from throughout their life. Even after this transfer, let's not forget that the death benefit is still active on the parent's or grandparent's life if the child continues making at least minimum premium payments. When the insured person eventually dies, the child will receive the death benefit with instructions how to use it to start Personal Banks for their children. This can provide an opportunity to start a generational wealth-building system that will make each generation potentially wealthier than its predecessors. You can create a financial independence legacy for your family using your Personal Bank.

This is a permanent whole life policy where your annual premiums never increase. In term life and universal life insurance policies the annual premiums increase as you get older and eventually the cost of the premiums become unsustainable. Because this is a high cash value policy you can choose to stop your premium payments after just a few years allowing your premiums to be paid by the increasing growth of cash value from your guaranteed returns and dividends. If you do so you will miss out on all that tax-deferred growth and tax-free income that you would have had by continuing to fund your policy.

One of the main purposes of your Personal Bank is to pay off your debts. Every dollar you use to eliminate your debts remains in your bank, accumulating interest and dividends even when you borrow from the policy to pay off debts. The cash value in the policy acts also as an emergency fund. At the end of the process, your debts are paid off, and all the dollars you used to do it with are still in your bank, continually growing. This is also the one of the best options to transfer wealth and create a legacy for your children or grandchildren. The Personal Bank should be maximized before investing in the market because it has the following advantages:

- It is one of the safest investments, where all growth is tax free and guaranteed.
- The Personal Bank provides a tax-free vehicle to safely put the excess money that becomes available when you become debt free which is significantly higher than the limits that can be put on a retirement plan.
- Tax-free removes the uncertainty of what increase taxes could do to your retirement plan savings when you need the money the most and are the most vulnerable because you are not working.
- At the time of this writing, it has a guaranteed 4+% tax-deferred rate of return and a guaranteed locked in 5% loan rate.
- Many big-name advisors recommend you buy term insurance and invest the difference. However, many individuals don't invest the difference but spend it. The Personal Bank has built in self-discipline, ensuring you do have money in retirement.
- You may also have access to the life insurance benefits before you pass away should you have a terminal illness, critical illness or chronic illness making the policy like a long-term care policy.
- You never have to worry about the volatility of the stock market.
- You have guaranteed insurability for your life and when you die, the death benefit goes 100% tax-free to your heirs.

- You have access to the cash value in the policy without penalties or restrictions.
- You reverse the flow of interest you are paying to the bank back to paying the interest to yourself.
- You pay no income and capital-gains taxes on policy loans and most withdrawals.
- It does not require any dramatic lifestyle changes and provides money for purchases and retirement needs.
- The interest and dividends are paid on all the money you have put into the policy, even if you have borrowed money from the policy to spend.
- The owner and the insured do not have to be the same person. The wife can be the owner of the policy and the insured could be her husband or child. If sole owner, she has complete control of the cash value in the policy and not the insured. If health and age do not allow you to get the insurance you need, you own the insurance policy on the life of another person.
- The death benefit is a great side benefit to these policies. It can be critical to leave a legacy and to care for your family and can be a jump start of future wealth for your family. As the cash value grows your death benefit also grows. The older you get, the more money is passed on to your family. You have unrestricted liquidity, control and use of your money for any reason.
- There is great flexibility in the policy. Many people mistakenly think that you must pay premiums each year into a whole life policy to keep it active. This is just not true. You can frontload your policy with high premium payments for 2 to 4 years and then the policy is paid in full You can also reduce the amount you pay into the policy each year if you have restricted cash flow, just pay the basic premium. When you have more money, put more in. There is great flexibility and a good insurance agent can help you

with your questions.

- In many states, these assets are protected from creditors, judgments and lawsuits.
- You can build your wealth tax free and access your wealth tax free (provided a MEC does not occur or a lapse or surrender with a gain as this would result in a taxable event).
- It helps you pay off debt, invest, and save at the same time. Pay off your cars, home, student loans and credit cards while simultaneously building retirement wealth using the same dollars.

Here is an example of a high cash value whole life policy for a 40-year-old female non-smoker with annual premiums of $10,000. Note that the cash value always continues to grow as well as the death benefit. At age 65 her cash value has grown to $445,154 with a death benefit of $882,514. If she started at age 30, and put in $30,000 for 25 years, her cash value would be over $2,166,549 and have a death benefit of well over $3 million at age 65. If we use the example family in this book, who after paying off their debt, will have over $30,000 annually to put toward their Personal Bank. By age 65 they would have over $1,333,462 in cash value and a death benefit of over $2.6 million. Remember, they always have available that additional $30,000 each year in their cash value to buy cars, take vacations and send their children to college while the cash value in their policy is always growing. When you become debt free, you could easily put much more into your Personal Bank such as $20,000, $30,000 or even $100,000 a year depending on your income. You will never worry about what the stock market is doing knowing that your financial and retirement needs have been guaranteed and you will be leaving a legacy for your family. Note that there is a guaranteed portion which you can always count on and the current assumption based on recent dividends which you most likely would receive.

40 YEAR OLD MALE. MASS MUTUAL POLICY. $10,000/YR — 25 YEARS						
		AGE/FUNDING		GUARANTEED		CURRENT ASSUMPTIONS	
Yr	Age	Annual Outlay	Cum. Outlay	Cash Value	Death Benefit	Cash Value	Death Benefit
1	41	$10,000	$10,000	$8,463	$277,680	$8,609	$277,680
2	42	$10,000	$20,000	$16,970	$304,425	$17,653	$304,903
3	43	$10,000	$30,000	$26,449	$330,269	$27,929	$331,688
4	44	$10,000	$40,000	$36,350	$355,250	$38,866	$358,072
5	45	$10,000	$50,000	$46,533	$379,402	$50,360	$384,093
6	46	$10,000	$60,000	$56,999	$402,760	$62,418	$409,804
7	47	$10,000	$70,000	$67,758	$425,357	$75,063	$435,241
8	48	$10,000	$80,000	$78,814	$447,226	$88,325	$460,441
9	49	$10,000	$90,000	$90,216	$468,393	$102,235	$485,444
10	50	$10,000	$100,000	$101,966	$488,883	$116,822	$510,203
11	51	$10,000	$110,000	$114,064	$508,718	$132,137	$534,736
12	52	$10,000	$120,000	$126,490	$527,921	$148,190	$559,131
13	53	$10,000	$130,000	$139,218	$546,515	$165,026	$583,397
14	54	$10,000	$140,000	$152,234	$564,526	$182,668	$607,610
15	55	$10,000	$150,000	$165,503	$581,977	$201,164	$631,795
16	56	$10,000	$160,000	$178,896	$598,895	$220,559	$656,056
17	57	$10,000	$170,000	$192,499	$615,304	$204,979	$680,456
18	58	$10,000	$180,000	$206,291	$631,227	$262,450	$705,000
19	59	$10,000	$190,000	$220,346	$646,686	$285,021	$729,699
20	60	$10,000	$200,000	$234,632	$661,700	$308,752	$754,461
21	61	$10,000	$210,000	$249,103	$676,284	$333,614	$779,344
22	62	$10,000	$220,000	$263,673	$690,457	$359,637	$804,482
23	63	$10,000	$230,000	$278,250	$704,238	$386,889	$829,973
24	64	$10,000	$240,000	$292,769	$717,647	$415,385	$855,976
25	65	$10,000	$250,000	$307,217	$730,702	$445,154	$882,514
26	66	$0		$315,137	$563,277	$467,580	$835,756
30	70	$0		$347,400	$563,277	$568,407	$921,512
35	75	$0		$347,440	$563,277	$722,183	$1,046,976
40	80	$0		$427,978	$563,277	$909,880	$1,197,526
45	85	$0		$462,366	$563,277	$1,132,824	$1,380,062
50	90	$0		$489,882	$563,277	$1,386,201	$1,598,884

Below are four condensed charts of the 40-year-old female non-smoker comparing putting in $10,000, $25,000, $50,000 and $100,000 each year into their Personal Bank. At age 65, the dentist that put in $10,000 a year will have $445,154 in cash value and $882,514 in death benefits. If she would've put in $25,000 per year she would have $1,112,884 in cash value and $2,206,286 in death benefit at age 65. If she would've put in $50,000 per year she would have $2,225,760 in cash value and $4,412,572 in death benefit at age 65. And if she was able to put in $100,000 each year she would have had $4,451,536 in cash value and $8,825,143 in death benefit. When doctors become debt free and run a profitable practice it would not be hard to have an extra $100,000 or even $200,000 that they could put in this tax-deferred, tax-free savings account to fund their life.

40 YEAR OLD MALE. MASS MUTUAL POLICY— 25 YEARS					
Yr	Age	Annual Outlay	Cum. Outlay	Cash Value	Death Benefit
1	41	$10,000	$10,000	$8,609	$277,680
5	45	$10,000	$50,000	$50,360	$384,093
10	50	$10,000	$100,000	$116,822	$510,203
15	55	$10,000	$150,000	$201,164	$631,795
20	60	$10,000	$200,000	$308,752	$754,461
25	65	$10,000	$250,000	$445,154	$882,514
26	66	0	$250,000	$467,580	$835,756
30	70	0	$250,000	$568,407	$921,512
35	75	0	$250,000	$722,183	$1,046,976
40	80	0	$250,000	$909,880	$1,197,526
45	85	0	$250,000	$1,132,824	$1,380,062
50	90	0	$250,000	$1,386,201	$1,593,884

40 YEAR OLD MALE. MASS MUTUAL POLICY— 25 YEARS				
Yr	Age	Annual Outlay	Cum. Outlay	Cash Value	Death Benefit
1	41	$25,000	$25,000	$21,523	$694,201
5	45	$25,000	$125,000	$125,900	$960,233
10	50	$25,000	$250,000	$292,054	$1,275,506
15	55	$25,000	$375,000	$502,910	$1,579,487
20	60	$25,000	$500,000	$771,880	$1,886,154
25	65	$25,000	$625,000	$1,112,884	$2,206,286
26	66	0	$625,000	$1,168,951	$2,089,390
30	70	0	$625,000	$1,421,017	$2,303,779
35	75	0	$625,000	$1,805,457	$2,617,440
40	80	0	$625,000	$2,274,701	$2,993,816
45	85	0	$625,000	$2,832,060	$3,450,155
50	90	0	$625,000	$3,465,501	$3,984,709

40 YEAR OLD MALE. MASS MUTUAL POLICY— 25 YEARS				
Yr	Age	Annual Outlay	Cum. Outlay	Cash Value	Death Benefit
1	41	$50,000	$50,000	$43,047	$1,388,401
5	45	$50,000	$250,000	$251,801	$1,920,466
10	50	$50,000	$500,000	$584,108	$2,551,013
15	55	$50,000	$750,000	$1,005,820	$3,158,974
20	60	$50,000	$1,000,000	$1,543,760	$3,772,307
25	65	$50,000	$1,250,000	$2,225,768	$4,412,572
26	66	0	$1,250,000	$2,337,902	$4,178,780
30	70	0	$1,250,000	$2,842,034	$4,607,558
35	75	0	$1,250,000	$3,610,915	$5,234,879
40	80	0	$1,250,000	$4,549,402	$5,987,632
45	85	0	$1,250,000	$5,664,119	$6,900,310
50	90	0	$1,250,000	$6,931,003	$7,969,418

40 YEAR OLD MALE. MASS MUTUAL POLICY— 25 YEARS					
Yr	Age	Annual Outlay	Cum. Outlay	Cash Value	Death Benefit
1	41	$100,000	$100,000	$86,094	$2,776,803
5	45	$100,000	$500,000	$503,602	$3,840,932
10	50	$100,000	$1,000,000	$1,168,215	$5,102,025
15	55	$100,000	$1,500,000	$2,011,640	$6,317,948
20	60	$100,000	$2,000,000	$3,087,520	$7,544,614
25	65	$100,000	$2,500,000	$4,451,536	$8,825,143
26	66	0	$2,500,000	$4,675,805	$8,357,561
30	70	0	$2,500,000	$5,684,068	$9,215,116
35	75	0	$2,500,000	$7,221,830	$10,469,758
40	80	0	$2,500,000	$9,098,805	$11,975,263
45	85	0	$2,500,000	$11,328,238	$13,800,619
50	90	0	$2,500,000	$13,862,005	$15,938,836

It is not recommended that you ever close the policy because you will lose the death benefit and be required to pay taxes on anything above what you have contributed (cost basis). To learn more about the infinite banking and how to create your own Personal Bank check out personalbank4U.com.

Option 2: Conservative, Low-Risk, Low-Return Investments

If you are risk-averse, cannot take a 10% to 20% drop in the market, and you need your money to live on in the next five to seven years, then you should invest more in CDs, bonds, and US treasuries. Do not put this money in bond mutual funds or ETFs because of their recent low returns and rising interest rates. The following are your better options:

Option 2a: Schwab money-market account (SWVXX) is a good interim place for your money while you are waiting to buy index funds. As of this writing, their 7-day yield is about

2.3%. These are not FDIC insured, but they are SIPC insured up to $500,000. This fund is available for individual retirement and investment accounts. If your account is a corporation, trust or 401(k), then you would use either the Schwab Government Money Fund (SWVXX) or the Schwab Treasury Obligations Money Fund (SNOXX), both currently returning about 2%.

Option 2b: Short-term treasury bills or notes and FDIC-insured CDs. These investments are considered truly safe for those who do not want to take any risk and need funds available within the next five to seven years. When this book was written in April 2019, the daily treasury yield curve rates for six months was around 2.4%, and for one year the rates were about 2.6%, which barely keeps up with inflation. You can buy these online through treasurydirect.gov or through Charles Schwab and pay no commission. If you choose to work with one of the Schwab brokers, the trade will be $25. If you worry about fluctuations in the stock market, this is a good place to put your money. A Treasury Bill (T-Bill) is a short-term debt obligation backed by the Treasury Department of the US government that matures in less than one year. Other Treasury notes have maturities from two to ten years, while Treasury bonds have maturities of greater than 10 years. These both pay interest semi-annually, and the only real difference between Treasury notes and bonds is their maturity length. I recommend Treasuries over bond-exchange-traded funds ETFs because treasury bills are guaranteed. In 2018 the return for a one-year Treasury was more than 2% while the US bond fund was a -0.03%.

Option 3: S&P 500 or the total US stock market index mutual funds or ETFs — High Risk, High Return.

Because 80% to 90% of your total assets are in inflation adjusted assets such as your paid off home and business, Personal

Bank and income, you can put 10% to 20% of your liquid assets into riskier assets such as index funds. To me, these two index funds are considered the gold standard of stock market investments, as they perform better than 96% of all other actively managed mutual funds. Warren Buffett has said that before he dies, he will put the inheritance for his children into a Vanguard S&P 500 fund and recommend they do not touch it. Buffett does not worry about economic analysis when buying a stock or company. It is all about buying the right company at the **right price** and then holding that company forever. That is why he buys when the company or market is down (buy low).

My personal strategy is to keep most of my investing money in my Personal Bank with cash value earning near 5% and short term money in my Schwab money market account earning around 2% and wait to purchase my S&P 500 index fund when there is a 10% drop in the market. If the market drops further, I find more money to buy more. This is not trying to time the market and get in and out but just buying low when stocks are on sale. Once I buy these funds I always keep them and do not sell. 2018 was a very volatile year for the market which had a couple of over 10% drops in the S&P 500. Because I had funds stored in my money market account and Personal Bank, I was able to take advantage of the 10% to 20% drop and was rewarded with a 10% to 20% increase during the rebound in the S&P 500 index fund. Once I buy the S&P 500 index fund, I do not sell it but keep it forever and continue to add to my portfolio during these downturn opportunities (see table on next page).

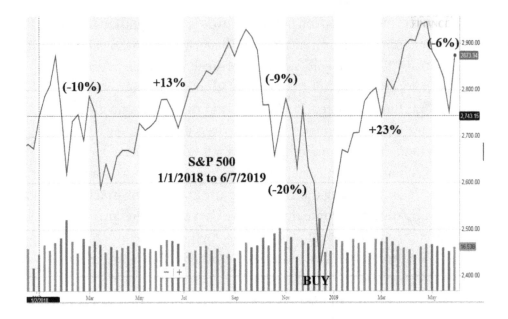

Both Vanguard and Schwab have both S&P 500 index mutual funds and ETFs with minimal fees. You can buy the Schwab S&P 500 index mutual fund (ticker symbol SWPPX) at the expense ratio of 0.03%, or the Vanguard 500 index mutual fund (ticker symbol VFIAX) with an expense ratio of 0.04%, both providing an average annual return over the past 10-year period of about 15.4% (see chart below). Or you can buy Schwab US Broad Total Market index mutual fund (ticker symbol SWTSX), at the expense ratio of 0.03%, or the Vanguard Total Stock Market Index ETF (ticker symbol VTI), with expense ratio of 0.04%, both returning an average annual return over a 10-year period of 15.5%. The average 15-year return for both S&P 500 and the US stock market index was only 8.6% and 8.9% because of the 2008 market crash. These before tax returns are like the tax-free returns that you get in the Personal Bank (which also has a death benefit). The market can be volatile and that is why I recommend most of your assets be in safe, inflation adjusted bond-like vehicles such as your paid off home, paid off business, steady income, and Personal Bank with only 10% to 20% invested in your market gambling fund with the S&P 500 index or the total US stock market index. Then you're done; relax and enjoy life.

Comparing average annual returns for Schwab and Vanguard Index funds 4/1/2019 (Morningstar.com)								
	S&P 500 Index				Total US Stock Market Index			
	Vanguard S&P 500 MF	Vanguard S&P 500 ETF	Schwab S&P 500 MF	Schwab S&P 500 like ETF	Schwab Total US Stock MF	Schwab Total US Stock ETF	Vanguard Total US Stock MF	Vanguard Total US Stock ETF
Ticker symbol	VFIAX	VOO	SWPPX	SCHX	SWTSX	SCHB	VTSAX	VTI
Expense ratio	0.04%	0.04%	0.03%	0.03%	0.03%	0.03%	0.04%	0.04%
# of stocks	509	509	509	771	2728	2432	3680	3680
1 year	11.3%	11.3%	11.3%	11.3%	10.5%	10.7%	10.7%	10.8%
3 years	14.4%	14.4%	14.4%	14.6%	14.4%	14.5%	14.5%	14.5%
5 years	12.1%	12.1%	12.0%	12.0%	11.6%	11.7%	11.7%	11.6%
10 years	15.4%		15.3%		15.5%		15.5%	15.5%
15 Years	8.6%		8.6%		8.9%		8.9%	8.9%

In 2017, I attended Berkshire Hathaway's annual meeting in Omaha, Nebraska. I sat about 70 feet from Warren Buffett when he told us about the bet he'd made with one of the large hedge fund managers in 2007. He bet the fund manager of Protégé Partners $1 million to be given to charity that the S&P 500 would beat a basket of hedge funds over the next decade. Warren Buffett looked out at the large crowd of 40,000 attendees and divided us in half. He said to those of us on the right side of the room that we were just average investors who could afford to put our money only in an index fund such as the S&P 500 and would settle for whatever it produced. But the 20,000 attendees on the left had a lot of available money; some were millionaires and could afford to pay 4.3% of their assets in fees to a hedge-fund manager and 3% to hedge-fund brokers each year to get extremely high returns. The fees paid to these hedge funds would average $98 billion a year.

Ten years after that bet, in 2017, the S&P 500 index fund had compounded an annual gain of 8.5% over the 10 years, beating the average increase of 2.4% earned by the basket of funds selected by Protégé Partners. This is another example of keeping it simple and staying away from high fees.

Remember to Stop the Noise

I recommend that you only start investing when you are completely debt free, because paying off debt gives you the highest rate of return without risk or fees. As you create a business model, you will find all the abundance that you need and will never think about so-called "retirement." Continue to invest each month in your Personal Bank and add to your stock portfolio when you see a greater-than 10% drop in the market — this is the best time to buy. And never get out of the market during these drops. A YouTube clip from the classic television series *Bob Newhart,* "Stop it," reminds us to stop our negative self-talk, worries and anxieties over investing and what's happening in the market. Stop listening to the financial news and focus on living and enjoying life. If you want true peace, stop listening to all the news. Once you have implemented *Dr. Ace's Financial Freedom Guide*, you can focus your energies on what you love, including the people in your life.

Chapter 9*:

ENJOY LIFE, LIBERTY, AND
THE PURSUIT OF HAPPINESS

*THE MOST IMPORTANT CHAPTER

Enjoying Good Health

About three years ago I noticed that my computer IT guy had lost a considerable amount of weight. He was six foot two, and when I first met him, he weighed around 300 pounds. Within six months, he had dropped 100 pounds and now looked great. I was amazed because I disliked exercise and had always had trouble losing weight, so I asked him what his secret was.

He told me that weight loss was pretty much 90% diet and 10% exercise. He said he changed his eating habits and moved to a high-fat, low-carbohydrate, ketogenic method of eating. He recommended a site called Dietdoctor.com, which was founded in 2011 and has over 55,000 members worldwide, making it the largest low-carb site in the world. It is filled with many articles, experts, videos, and low-carb recipes.

At that time, I was five foot six and weighed about 200 pounds, with a beautiful pot belly. Within three months of taking his advice,

I lost over thirty-five pounds and have maintained my weight at 165 pounds for the past three years. I walk a couple of miles once a week and do some weightlifting two times a week to keep my muscle tone. I take multivitamins, vitamin D, magnesium, and fish oil. I can now sleep eight hours a night, and I feel better than I have for years.

Another great website to help transform your health is http:// drhyman.com/. Dr. Mark Hyman is an American physician and a *New York Times* bestselling author. He is the founder and medical director of the Ultra Wellness Center and director of the Cleveland Clinical Center for Functional Medicine. His books and audios on understanding functional medicine can change your life. See Appendix A.

Creating Great Relationships

Warren Buffett gives the following advice. *"Be around people that you admire and enjoy. They usually have an upbeat attitude about life, they're humorous, have integrity and are generous people who are thinking about what they can do for you. These qualities that you admire are not innate at birth, and you can acquire them. Then there are those negative qualities that turn you off in people who always need to be right and that you don't enjoy being with. You can choose what person you want to be, so why not choose the person you admire? Take your five best friends, mentors or your heroes, and write down the qualities that you like about them. Incorporate these qualities in your life and eliminate the qualities of the people that turn you off. It's that simple. It is important to work with people in your life and you will get the best out of people if they like you. You need to develop these habits now. Incorporate the great qualities now and eliminate the bad qualities and you will have an incredible life. Choose your heroes very carefully because they will define you. You are one of your children's favorite hero."*

Buffett also said that the secret to long-lasting relationships is low expectations. A friend told me that relationships improved immensely when you give up the need to be right. My wife, Nancy, and I were married in 1969. We have five children and thirteen grandchildren. We have had our ups and downs, but we are very supportive of each other. And if she has a problem that I know I can fix immediately, I listen intently and never offer advice. (There is a great and funny YouTube clip called *"It's Not About the Nail"* that makes this point very clear.)

Another great book is *The Five Love Languages,* by Gary Chapman. The five love languages are words of positive affirmation, acts of service, receiving gifts, quality time, and physical touch. Because I was abandoned as a child, my language is positive affirmation. This will fill up my love tank, while criticism will empty it. Even though I do some stupid things sometimes, Nancy is not critical of my errors. My wife's love language is quality time and acts of service. If she has something for me to do, such as change the burnt-out light bulb in the kitchen, I immediately do it.

When I see my underwear drawer full, I know she did the laundry, and I thank her. I often tell her how beautiful she is and how much I love her. Even though our children may do things that we do not like, we provide advice only when asked, are never judgmental or critical, and are there to love them no matter what happens in their lives. Warren Buffett said he never met a truly successful person who did not have a great relationship with their children. Are you truly successful?

One last comment: I would never be in a relationship that is toxic or does not add true meaning to my life. Sadly, this toxicity could be from parents who are always judgmental and critical of you. Tell any toxic person that if they continue to be judgmental or critical you will not be seeing them. I give you permission to take care of yourself first, or else you will not be good to anyone else. Think about what you are teaching your children about the type of relationship they should be in.

Creating love in your life

Love is that special feeling we get when we have a connection with people and things in our life. It is created when we initiate and give love to people and things. Somebody could love us, but we may not feel anything, but we always feel love when we are loving others. We are fortunate to be in a profession where we can love our patients, our team, what we do and especially our family. This doesn't just apply to loving people but also things in our lives such as a good movie, a book, a special mug and other things we go back to and create that feeling of love. Like the movie, "Love Actually" is all around us.

Learning and Understanding Meditation

Meditation helps reduce your stress, increase your energy, clear your brain and relax the body for a deeper more restful sleep. It makes you feel more connected, less anxious, and helps you to be calmer and more clear-headed in demanding situations. It can help you experience better relationships and sharpens your life focus. To learn a simple and powerful form of meditation, I recommend the new book written by Emily Fletcher entitled, *Stress Less, Accomplish More: Meditation for Extraordinary Performance*. For a better understanding of the Zeva Technique of meditation, check out her website: https://zivameditation.com/online/ or watch her YouTube video https://www.youtube.com/watch?v=yy6uOoMzbPg.

Letting Go of Issues and Emotional Pain From Your Past

When I was three years old my mother divorced my father and he moved to another city. My mother had to go back to school to get her degree and my brothers and I lived with my grandmother for the next five years. At that young age I subconsciously blamed myself for their divorce because if I could had been a better little boy this would not have happened. I carried this shame and pain through adulthood hoping that no one would find out how bad I was. I subconsciously stuffed this emotional pain and started to feel from my brain, not my heart, where there was no pain. This inability to feel deep emotions affected many in my personal and business relationships. I can easily understand why many men are not emotional. Once I addressed these issues and let go of much of my emotional pain, which we can be easily done with proper techniques, my life and myself became more emotionally alive and peaceful. Many people carry deeply embedded emotional pain from their past that affects and controls their lives. This could be from abandonment (divorce), which I experienced, sexual abuse, not being wanted and there are many more. One group I worked with who are exceptionally good in helping individuals to identify, address and let go of these issues is Legacy Life Consulting. Contact them at: https://www.legacylifeconsulting.com/ David Stamation (208) 946-3894.

You Need to Take Care of Yourself First

Many people have been taught that to serve others they need to give away all their time and energies first before they take care of themselves, leaving them feeling exhausted, frustrated and angry. This is especially true with women. This is very sad. The fact is, you can better serve and help others if you take care of your own needs first. Taking care of yourself is the least selfish thing you can do. You cannot pour from the empty cup. You need to set time aside every day to love and nurture yourself resulting in you feeling happier and less resentful as you serve others. The magic word that you need to use more often is "No", I cannot do that, thanks for asking.

Teaching Your Children about Finances

Mahatma Gandhi was asked what his message to the world was. He said, "My life is my message." Teach your children the satisfaction of being a saver instead of a spender. You need to show them the satisfaction of accomplishment and doing a job well. Be the example for them of how they can find fun and joy in everything they do, instead of teaching them duty, responsibility and that you must work hard for living.

Teach your children to understand the ideas in this book. Create a job for them in your office so that they can fund a Roth IRA. Schwab is a great place to put this money because there is no minimum to open an account and are no fees when trading among their funds and ETFs. Any money your child makes, you can match. When the children are old enough, age ten or eleven, teach them the simple investing approach found in this book. William Bernstein, in his book, *The Investor's Manifesto,* suggests you set up a small portfolio with index funds in each child's name. Teach them how to file their account statements, log in and print out reports. Every quarter, set up an investment meeting with them and discuss portfolio performance. The most important thing you can leave your heirs will not be cold, hard cash, but rather the ability to save, spend and invest prudently. Reward them with the dividends and half of the capital appreciation of their stock funds. Let them experience both the ups and downs of the market and help them with their emotions showing them stocks that just came on sale. Andrew Tobias, in Chapter 10 of his book, The Only Investment Guide You'll Ever Need, has some great ideas on teaching your children about finances.

I knew one dentist who helped his daughter fund her IRA each year from age one by using the money she earned as a model for pictures in his office. He later had her work in his practice. By age thirty they had put in $101,500 and her Roth IRA was worth over $450,000.

Finding Happiness

When we get to be between forty and fifty years old, our lives change. Many of us go through a clinical depression because we have lost the excitement of starting our careers or our practices. Things may be going smoothly. The kids may be in college. But life changes, even if we don't want to admit it. We don't make changes in our work life anymore, and we don't care if it gets any better; we just hope it doesn't get any worse. Sometimes we take up hobbies instead of creating excitement in our work lives. As we reach midlife, it's time to realize that this is it; it's not going to get any better; it's all in our minds. We need to recognize this is as an opportunity to go to work happy every day, and to change our relationship to work so that it is fun. Life can be exciting if we let it be.

The future does not exist except in our imaginations, and the past is merely a trace in our minds. The brain changes our recollections to fit our own convenience and purposes. This is also true with our work lives. Once we understand that we are working on a day-to-day basis, not a year-to-year basis, our attitudes and philosophies change, and incidentally, we become more prosperous and have more fun.

I have consistently found that those who were happy while they were working are also happy during their retirement years. The opposite is also true: those who did not enjoy their work don't find happiness in retirement any more than they did while they were working.

The life and business coach, Kendrick Mercer, once had a fifty-year-old client from North Carolina. The client told him that he had hated dentistry for the past twenty-five years. The worst problem was that he could not quit because he owed so much money. Kendrick told him that he could set up his finances to be economically free in ten years, but he knew his client's problem was deeper than finances, so he asked him, "Once you reach financial freedom, what are you going to do?"

"I would first quit my practice," the client told him.

"Then what are you going to do?" Mercer asked.

"I am going to golf," he replied.

"Then what are you going to do?" Mercer asked.

He said, "I will buy a place on the beach and walk on the beach."

"Great," Mercer said. "Then what are you going to do?"

"Then I will watch TV and read books."

"Then what are you going to do?" Mercer asked him one more time.

He became sad and somber and said, "I will just walk on the beach some more."

"Great! What are you going to do then?"

He started to cry and said, "I'm going to die."

This is a pretty sad story. There was no real aliveness to this man, just a dead story. Mercer's fifty-year-old client was trying to get someplace instead of loving his life.

Mercer told him, "My job is to assist you in knowing that life is never going to be any better or worse than it is right now. It's just how you're looking at it. For you to go back and spend one more day losing your life for some future time which does not sound all that exciting will make your life a failure."

The client did not like hearing this, but he knew it was true. Mercer told him to go home and change his mind and outlook so he could enjoy dentistry again, and appreciate his patients, his staff, and all his relationships. If he did this and still did not enjoy dentistry, then he should quit, sell everything and do something with his life that he enjoyed.

The dentist friend did go back and created a new story for himself and his practice, and then he began to enjoy his practice. Kendrick coached him to slow down and sell some things to get rid of his debt. The client finally started to relax. Because life is lived in the present, it will truly never get any better or worse than it is this minute. It's all a matter of how we look at our experiences. This principle is the same for each one of us.

I know endodontists who have become debt-free and financially secure. Yet many tell me that they are not happy. What I learned from Kendrick Mercer is that we carry many family imprints, negative emotional experiences such as abandonment or abuse, that make us feel that we are not worthy of happiness. We need to address these issues and let go of the loss and pain from the past. Sometimes, we need counseling to help us through this process.

One company that I have worked with which has helped me and many doctors and their team members in identifying what holds them back from enjoying and finding peace in every aspect of their lives, resulting in more peace and happiness, is Legacy Life Consulting (http://legacylifeconsulting.com/).

It's Never Too Late

You may be in your 50s or even 60s and feel stuck in your practice, and in your life. Just like the story above, you can reassess your practice and life, and make changes now. I've worked with many endodontists in their 50s and 60s helping them through the process of making their practice more efficient and fun while working fewer days. We also talked about getting rid of the junk in your life. Junk is defined anything that does not add meaning to your life.

First, find out what your net worth is by writing down all your assets and debts (appendix B). Look at your practice and eliminate everything that does not make it fun. This may include team members who are negative and cause you drama. Eliminate and refer out all procedures that cause you stress, such as extractions or root canals. Write a letter to the 20% of your patients that cause you 80% of your grief. Set them free from your practice while providing a certain amount of days for emergency care. Each state's dental association will have an example of this letter that you can use. Before you begin the process, you may want to hire a practice management consultant to help you. This consultant can help you become much more efficient in your practice and may recommend procedures to control other conditions, such as sleep apnea, that can become a profit center. Once you become much more profitable, you could decide to sell your practice and move to a different part of the country where it may be warmer or where you can be closer to your children and work part-time. When you clear your mind and are open to all possibilities, the choices become endless.

As you go through this process, make sure that you have your spouse on board. Some of the junk that you may want to eliminate may include the large boat that you only use two to three weeks out of the year but costs you $1,000 in slip fees and maintenance each month. You may have had a loss in an individual investment such as a stock or limited partnership. Realize that you already have taken the loss, and chances are great that it will never come back. But by you keeping this loss it distracts you from moving on and learning from your lesson. So just sell it and use the loss to offset your gains in other investments. The only exception are stocks that drop during a down market, because you never sell in a down market. You may have rental property that causes you a lot of headaches and low financial returns. It may be the large house with high maintenance costs which you could sell and move into a new or smaller home or condo and invest the difference in your retirement account. Go through your closet and get rid of all clothes and shoes that you have not worn in the past year. Getting rid of junk in your life gives you great peace of mind and contentment. Now you can focus on creating strong relationships with your spouse and your children.

What Percentage of Your Current Income Do You Need in Retirement?

Many financial advisors tell you that you need 70% of your current income to be comfortable in retirement. I think one reason they say this is to make sure you keep investing more money in their actively managed funds. You will probably only need somewhere between 25% to 35% of your current income. Let me summarize an excellent article by Dr. James Dahle in his website, White Coat Investor. https://www.whitecoatinvestor.com/Percentage-of-current-income-needed-in-retirement/

Do the math: Take your current income, let's say $200,000.

Subtract out 20% for taxes and 20% for retirement and you're down to $120,000.

Subtract out 5% for insurance, 5% for child-related costs, and 15% for your mortgage. You're now down to $70,000. Subtract out another 1% for job-related expenses, 2% for reduced charitable contributions, and 1% for reduced housing expenses. You're down to $62,000.

Add back in, say, 10% for increased travel costs and 5% for increased health care costs. This moves us up to $92,000. Subtract out $36,000 for Social Security and that leaves us at $56,000, or 28% of our current income. Using the 4% rule, $56,000 per year, adjusted for inflation, can be provided by retirement assets of $1.4 million. How long will it take for you to reach that goal if you save 20% of your $200K income a year and get a return of 5% real return on it? Around 21 years.

* * *

THE ILLUSION THAT MONEY WILL MAKE US HAPPY

Most Americans fall prey to the illusion that money will make us happy. But there are more miserable, depressed, and anxious millionaires than you can imagine! I've seen clearly and repeatedly that money will not buy happiness. Nothing that money can buy will make you happy on an ongoing basis, and many people resent those who have money. This attitude will prevent them from creating abundance in their lives.

The belief that money will make us happy seems almost unstoppable. It is one of the big illusions that keeps us from developing integrity with money. Some people think that if they win the lottery, they will be happy, but things never seem to work out that way. Money can make people miserable because of their false expectation of what it will bring. What makes us happy is having integrity in every aspect of our lives, including expressing our feelings through travel, love, and relationships.

On some level, we all know that money will not make us happy, but we still act as if it will. Money does bring a certain kind of security that we wouldn't otherwise have. With that security, perhaps we can express happiness or enjoy life more consistently. But being financially secure is different from being rich.

Happiness comes from enjoying each moment and appreciating everything that comes into our lives. It comes from helping others, such as our patients, our teams, and all others around us. This is where the real fun is. As we give love to others, we can't stop the abundance of love that comes into our own lives.

No precise dollar amount translates into this capacity. On the other hand, poor money management (such as having high debts and many creditors) can make you unhappy, and that is one good reason for developing a clear financial context. Sometimes it takes buying the things you always thought you wanted to realize that they alone do not bring you happiness. Spending without a clear guide diffuses and wastes your money and your financial freedom. If you have a clear context about money, you'll rent the boat or vacation home you've dreamed of first, to see if it really does add meaning to your life.

Jonathan Clements, in his must-read book, *The Little Book of Main Street – Money: 21 Simple Truths That Help Real People Make Real Money*, says that buying things might bring us happiness but not long-lasting happiness. Over the past decades we have made vast improvements in our standard of living, yet people still aren't any happier. We need to get off the treadmill and think about how we spend our money and how we spend our time. Clements makes six recommendations for happiness.

Buy experiences rather than things.

Count your blessings.

Strive for a sense of control.

Find a purpose instead of trying to have endless leisure.

Give a little, volunteer or donate.

Make time for friends and family.

His website has a wealth of information that is always updated and worth visiting. https://humbledollar.com/money-guide/main-menu/

Stop Complaining.

Half of the people think you deserve what you get, and the other half don't care. Kendrick Mercer shared a story with me after his three-month sailing from California to Lahaina, Maui. His trip was an incredible adventure with beautiful sunny days, stormy weather, moonbows at night and wonderful solitude. After arriving in Lahaina, he took a plane to Honolulu. He was enjoying the view over the ocean while a lady sitting next to him was complaining to him about her life, children and husband. During the break in her conversation he looked at her and said, "Let's play a game. Let's pretend the plane breaks right in half and we are all going to die. All you see in front of you is blue sky. We have two choices: we can grab on to the armrest in terror and think about all the things we didn't do in our life, or we can calmly unbuckle our seatbelts, stand up, jump forward and fly for the rest of our lives." She did not say much after that but gave him a big hug at the end of the flight. Why not live our life in gratitude and enjoy every moment?

Cultural and Family Imprinting

I realized that before my clients could be at peace with money, they had to open and address the deeper behavioral issues keeping them from having integrity with money and with life.

Our attitudes toward money can keep us from living full and peaceful lives. We have all inherited a range of imprints from our families of origin concerning money. These imprints often including prejudices, insecurities, and false assumptions, which pull us away from developing integrity with money. We tend to repeat the clichés about money that we learned as children, even if they're not true, such as "You can never have enough money," "It takes money to make money," "The poor working man can never get ahead," and "You must work hard for your money."

Most people who have plenty of money keep working, not because they enjoy it or choose to, but because working has come to represent worthiness. It is a kind of cultural fad. Work seems to justify our very right to exist. The family imprint duty, responsibility and working hard for a living, may be incredibly strong, or perhaps work has become an addiction. Many people work because that is what society expects them to do, or because their parents told them they'd be bums if they didn't work hard six days a week. Our current attitudes about money tend to limit our choices even when we have achieved wealth. The ideal balance would be to have a great deal of money and at the same time to be at peace, doing only what we really want to do. For most of us, our lives are half over, and it is time to have some fun now! You cannot create what you cannot envision. Get very clear about making your life fun and enjoyable, feel it and keep moving toward that vision. Bring your vision to your office and your family, and don't settle for anything less. Take time to talk to your children not about duty or responsibility but about what brings happiness, fun and joy in their lives, and what it will take to create that story for them.

How Do We Define Success?

This can be different for each one of us. For me, it is about loving what I do each day, being at peace in my life, being in good health, having time to be with and enjoy people I love, being debt-free, having enough money that I don't worry about money anymore, and having the time and resources to make a difference in the world around me. Others may define success as being the best dentist, making a lot of money, having time to do missionary work, retiring at age fifty-five, having $7 million in the bank, and the list goes on. This book is not meant to define your success but to show you how to have enough time and money to make choices in your life that are right for you. It's not about making a living, it is about making a life worth living.

French writer François-René de Chateaubriand (1768 to 1848) said, *"A master in the art of living draws no sharp distinction between his work and his play; his labor and his leisure; his mind and his body; his education and his recreation. He hardly knows which is which; he simply pursues his vision of excellence through whatever he is doing, and leaves others to determine whether he is working or playing. To himself, he always appears to be doing both."*

How Much Is Enough?

If you are like most people of the world, one bowl of rice a day would be enough. But here in America we think in terms of economic freedom. In my past book, *Time and Money*, I define economic freedom as the day you have accumulated enough safe, liquid assets that can reproduce your lifestyle income (the amount of money it takes to maintain your lifestyle), with safeguards against inflation, for the rest of your life without touching the principal. This will vary by individual, but once you are debt-free you could reach that point in five to seven years, by simply following the recommendations in this book.

Make a Difference in the World

There is difference between success and significance. One of the great advantages of having more time and more money is to make a difference in the lives of people in the world around us. One reason I enjoy going into the office two days a week is that I can create such abundance to share with others. Each year, I donate to many great causes including the Union Gospel Mission dental clinic for our street people, Safe Place for battered women, the food banks, a dental assisting program, my church and various other causes that make a difference in the world around me. I do believe that this even brings more abundance into my life. Even though you are working on paying off debt, donate either your time or money to an important cause. This will make a difference in your life and those you help.

The Two-Dollar-Bill Story of Happiness

I love giving out two-dollar bills as reminder of our freedom in the United States. This $2 bill is the only piece of US currency that depicts the same person on the front and on the back. On the front of the bill, we see Thomas Jefferson, the third president of the United States. Then we turn the bill over and him signing the Declaration of Independence. The people standing around the table are the committee who wrote the declaration. The main author is Thomas Jefferson (the tall person in the center). The person standing on the far left is John Adams, the second president of the United States.

John Adams and Thomas Jefferson had a few things in common: They were both presidents and were the only presidents who signed the Declaration of Independence. They both died on July 4th, within three hours of each other, exactly fifty years after they signed the Declaration of Independence.

FIGURE 8

In those days, the average man lived to age thirty-five. Adams was ninety and Jefferson was eighty-three on the day they died. I believe the reason they lived two to three generations beyond the average man is that they were both highly motivated to instill and imprint the ideals of freedom and independence into our American culture. They lived with a purpose.

This is why we live in one of the freest countries in the world and can work and live anywhere we want in this country. We are free to be in any mutual relationship we want, and to leave it if it is toxic (a relationship where you will never grow and are always being put down).

Sadly, most Americans don't know they are free. Many feel trapped in their lives, practice, jobs and relationships. They feel angry, controlled, frustrated, anxious or sad. These feelings come from a place of fear--- many people fear change and have one foot in and one foot out of their choices (relationships or jobs). These feelings immediately disappear when the person acts, after choosing to change, or by putting "both feet in or out" of their choice.

The $2 bill reminds us of our choice to be free, independent, and happy. The secret of happiness is in three choices. Any time you feel upset, angry, or trapped, there is something in your life that you are not accepting. The courage to make one of these three choices will give you back your freedom and peace of mind. The choices are as follows:

1. You can change your situation (relationship or work) which takes courage as you face and conquer your fears. For example, if someone is always judgmental or critical of you and this is a deal breaker, then you can tell them that behavior is no longer acceptable to you, and if they continue you will leave the relationship. If they stop this unacceptable behavior, then you will stay and be at peace. If not, you choose number two.

2. You can leave the situation (i.e., relationship or work).

3. If you can't change the situation or you choose not to leave the situation then you can stay and accept the "what is" of the situation and be totally at peace with the situation because it is your choice.

Summary

DR. ACE'S FINANCIAL FREEDOM

GUIDE IS VERY BASIC.

- First, write your new money story and set your goals for increasing your income, eliminating your debt first, and then increasing your savings and investments.
- Create a practice that you love, that is profitable, and then do more of it. Many dentist/owners that I coach complain about some of the people they work with who make them miserable. I tell them to go back to their office and tell the owner to fire those people. Then I remind them that they are the owner. Most people forget that they can make their practice exactly what they want it to be. They have the canvas and the brush.
- Learn to make more money and focus that money toward debt reduction. Once you are debt free, you should consider creating a Personal Bank. For more information go to personalbank4U. com. You can put any excess money into a Schwab money market account and take advantage of 10% or greater drops in the market, as occurred in 2018. Learn to invest on your own in a Schwab or Vanguard account in the United States market through index funds such as the S&P 500 or total US stock market. Once you feel comfortable investing on your own, share your knowledge and this book with other colleagues.Stop

listening to the news and worrying about what's happening in the market. This is just noise. That's it. Now, enjoy your life, give gratitude and spend the rest of your money on things that add meaning to your life. This leads to financial freedom and a life of self-integrity and peace.

- Economic peace of mind is more than just financial freedom. In fact, we can experience economic peace of mind long before we reach financial freedom. *Once we have a solid guide in place for achieving financial freedom, we can let go of our anxiety about money and live as if it has already happened.* With this newfound peace of mind, we can truly enjoy life in the moment because we are secure in what we have, and we know that we can deal with any life challenge.

We can face life with joy and excitement once we have a vision and a beautiful story for our lives. With *this book*, each of us can claim both financial freedom and economic and personal peace of mind. "Being happy is a choice."

Acknowledgments

To my wife, Nancy, who has always been supportive of my adventures and misadventures while creating an incredible life for myself and our children.

To my father, who showed me the problems with gambling and spending recklessly and died broke at age sixty-five. To my mother, who understood getting out of debt early, saving and investing safely, and who retired a millionaire, living to be eighty-seven.

To Cynthia Goerig the CEO of Endo Mastery and our head coach, Debra Miller who joined me 5 years ago to create a new and expanded vision for Endo Mastery and obtaining incredible success and results for our clients. To my cofounder, Todd Holmes who was my only coach for 17 years and made Endo Mastery possible. And to my newer coaches Trish Farrell and Jarrad Garrett who's outstanding care of our clients has made us the number one endodontic coaching program in the country.

To my financial mentors,

Kendrick Mercer, my coauthor on my last book, who taught me "If you have it made, why risk it?"—but more importantly taught me how to live my life in peace and contentment.

John Cummuta, who trained me on the importance of debt reduction.

Daniel R. Solin, who taught me the simplicity of just buying the S&P 500 index.

William Bernstein, whose down to earth investment books help me clarify my investment strategy through his humor and common-sense approach.

Warren Buffett, who has been an example of loving your work and living a great and simple life, and who taught me the importance of buying stocks on sale and keeping the investments forever.

Dr. Denny Southard who taught me the power and value of dividend investing.

Ben Franklin, one of our nation's founding fathers, who exemplified living frugally until you are out debt and creating prosperity through hard work and sound business principles. Author of The Way to Wealth.

To all those stupid financial mistakes I made as a dentist, which caused me great pain while giving me important lessons I remember well enough to share with you now.

To my athletic coaches (Mr. Bill Granger, Mr. Dick Truman, and Mr. Ralph Maughan) who taught me the importance of compassion and commitment of time and energy needed to help a person reach their highest potential.

To all my incredible clinical mentors (Drs. Jefferson Jones, Fred Seymour, Manny Wiseman, Joe Neaverth, Stephen Cohen, John McSpadden, Gary Carr, and Steve Buchanan) who saw the possibilities in a not-so-smart individual, allowing me to increase my clinical skills so I would have more satisfaction and fun in my profession over the years.

To my twenty-year Army experience, which helped mold my leadership skills and revealed the importance of empowering people.

To Dr. Arlen Lackey, who took me under his wing and trained me to deliver presentations at the national level.

To all my practice management coaches (Linda Miles, Dr. Mike Abernathy, Greg Stanley and Wes Warren, and Dr. Bill Blatchford), who helped me create a culture in my practice that is fun and profitable.

To Debra Miller, Alex Nottingham, Drs. Jim Kulild, Hugh Habas and Doug Carlsen who thoroughly reviewed my rough draft and gave me valuable insights and made important corrections.

To my publisher, John Koehler of Koehler Books and their editors, who helped make this possible.

Appendix A

RESOURCES FROM DR. ACE

Alexander, Michael A. *Stock Cycles: Why Stocks Won't Beat Money Markets Over the Next Twenty Years*. Writers Club Press, 2000.

Bernstein, William J. *If You Can: How Millennials Can Get Rich Slowly*. William J. Bernstein, 2014.

Bernstein, William J. *The Four Pillars of Investing: Lessons for Building a Winning Portfolio Hardcover*. McGraw Hill, 2010.

Bernstein, William J. *The Investor's Manifesto: Preparing for Prosperity, Armageddon, and Everything in Between*. John Wiley and Sons, Hoboken, NJ, 2010.

Bogle, John C. *The Little Book of Common Sense Investing: The Only Way to Guarantee Your Fair Share of Stock Market Returns*. Wiley, Hoboken, NJ, 2017.

Burnell, Dwayne. *Path to Financial Peace of Mind Paperback*. Bothell, WA. 2010

Chapman, Gary D. *The Five Love Languages: How to Express Heartfelt Commitment to Your Mate.* Thorndike Press, Waterville, ME, 2005. Clason, George S. The Richest Man in Babylon. Dauphin Publications, 2017.

Clements, Jonathan. *The Little Book of Main Street Money: 21 Simple Truths That Help Real People Make Real Money.* LLC Gildan Media, 2009.

Clements, Jonathan. Website: https://humbledollar.com/money-guide/main-menu/

Cummuta, John M. *Turn Your Debt into Wealth: A Proven System for Real Financial Freedom.* Simon & Schuster Audio, 2001.

Dahle, James M., MD. *The White Coat Investor: A Doctor's Guide to Personal Finance And Investing.* The White Coat Investor LLC, 2014.

Dahle, James M., MD. Website: https://www.whitecoatinvestor.com/

Farran, Howard. *Uncomplicate Business: All It Takes Is People, Time, and Money.* Greenleaf Book Group Press, Austin Texas. 2015.

Fletcher, Emily, *Stress Less, Accomplish More: Meditation for Extraordinary Performance.* HarperCollins Publishers, New York, NY. 2019

Goerig, Albert C., and Mercer, Kendrick. *Time and Money: Your Guide to Economic Freedom.* ACG Press, Olympia, WA, 2004.

Hyman, Mark. *Food: What the Heck Should I Eat?* Little, Brown and Company, 2018.

Hyman, Mark. *The Five Forces of Wellness: The Ultra Prevention System for Living an Active, Age-Defying, Disease-Free Life* Audio CD. 2006.

Headley, Jason. "It's Not About The Nail." YouTube. May 22, 2013. https://www.youtube.com/watch?v=-4EDhdAHrOg.

Malkiel, Burton Gordon, and Ellis, Charles D. *The Elements of Investing: Easy Lessons for Every Investor*. Wiley, Hoboken, NJ, 2013.
Malkiel, Burton Gordon. *A Random Walk Down Wall Street: The Time-tested Strategy for Successful Investing*. W.W. Norton & Company, New York, 2016.

Nash, R. Nelson. *Becoming Your Own Banker: Unlock the Infinite Banking Concept*. Infinite Banking Concepts LLC, Birmingham, AL. 2009

Parisi, Steve. YouTube: Infinite Banking 101: Live Webinar #1. 2018

Parisi, Steve. YouTube: Infinite Banking 101: Live Webinar #22 | Back to the Basics of the IBC. 2019

Phillips, David T. *The Family Bank Strategy: How to create your own personal Tax-Free bank and protect your estate from creditors and predators*. 2015

Robbins, Anthony, and Mallouk, Peter. *Unshakeable: Your Financial Freedom Playbook*. New York: Simon & Schuster, 2017.

Sinek, Simon. *Start with Why: How Great Leaders Inspire Everyone to Take Action*. Penguin Group, New York, NY. Dec 27, 2011.

Sinek, Simon. *Leaders Eat Last: Why Some Teams Pull Together and*

Others Don't. Penguin Group, New York, NY. May 23, 2017.

Solin, Daniel R. *The Smartest Investment Book You'll Ever Read: The Proven Way to Beat the "Pros" and Take Control of Your Financial Future.* Pedigree Books, New York, NY, 2010.

Solin, Daniel R. *The Smartest Money Book You'll Ever Read: Everything You Need to Know about Growing, Spending, and Enjoying Your Money.* Penguin Group, New York, NY 2011.

Solin, Daniel R. *The Smartest Retirement Book You'll Ever Read.* Penguin Group, New York, NY 2010.

Stanley, Thomas J. and Danko, William D. *Millionaire Next Door: The Surprising Secrets of America's Wealthy.* Taylor Trade Publishing, 2010.

Stanley, Thomas J. and Fallaw, Sarah Stanley. *The Next Millionaire Next Door: Enduring Strategies for Building Wealth.* The Rowan and Littlefield Publishing Group, 2019.

Swedroe, Larry E., and Hempen, Joe H. *The Only Guide to a Winning Bond Strategy You'll Ever Need: The Way Smart Money Preserves Wealth Today.* Saint Martin's Press, New York, 2006.

Thompson, Jake, *Money. Wealth. Life Insurance. How The Wealthy Use Life Insurance as a Tax-Free Personal Bank to Supercharge Their Savings.* Real wealth financial, 2013.

Thompson, Joshua, *The Simple Banking System: A Concise Look into Life Insurance As An Investment Tool. Becoming your own bank,* 2019.

Tobias, Andrew. *The Only Investment Guide You'll Ever Need*. Second Mariners books edition, New York, 2016.

Wattles, Wallace. *The Science of Getting Rich*. April, 1910.

Wright, Kelley. *Dividends Still Don't Lie: The Truth About Investing in Blue Chip Stocks and Winning in the Stock Market*. Wiley, Hoboken, NJ, 2010.

Yellen, Pamela. *The Bank On Yourself Revolution. Fire Your Banker, Bypass Wall Street, And Take Control Of Your Own Financial Future*. Benbella Books, Inc. Dallas, TX. 2016.

Zweig, Jason. *Your Money and Your Brain: How the New Science of Neuroeconomics Can Help Make You Rich*. Simon and Schuster, New York, NY, 2007.

Appendix B

STEP-BY-STEP DEBT REDUCTION PLAN

Act Today. Declaring that you are seriously committed to getting out of debt is the first step in achieving personal wealth. Go through the steps below. All forms can be downloaded from DoctorAce.com.

1. Sit down with your significant other: Both of you must be on board, knowing that this will strengthen your relationship, eliminate stress around money and give you back your freedom. Then read this book together, and then set time aside to do the following.

2. Add up your net worth, that is, everything you own, and then subtract everything you owe in the chart below.

DETERMINE YOUR NET WORTH			
ASSETS	AMOUNT	LIABILITIES	AMOUNT
Personal Cash (Bank)			
Practice Cash (Bank)			
Taxable Investments (stocks)			
Tax Deferred Investments (IRA/401K)			

Personal Bank- High cash value whole life insurance			
Gold/Silver			
Other			
Real Estate		How much is owed	
Main Home		How much is owed	
Vacation Homes		How much is owed	
Rental Property		How much is owed	
Practice Building		How much is owed	
Practice (60% of yearly collection)		How much is owed	
Other Assets		How much is owed	
Automobiles/ Boat		How much is owed	
Personal Property		How much is owed	
Pension (value = 20X yearly amt)		**School Loans**	
Social Security (value = 20X yearly amount)		**Credit cards debt**	
		Other debt	
Total assets $		**Total liabilities $**	

		Net worth $ (Assets-Liabilities)	

3. Write down your total household income.

Net income source (after taxes)	Earner A	Earner B
Salary (net, take-home pay)		
Part-time or self-employment income		
Home-based business income		
Investment income		
Social Security		
Pension		
Veteran's benefits		
Other		
Individual totals		

Total income of A and B		

4.   Reducing your monthly expenses. List all your current monthly expenses in the "current" column below. In the "reduced" column, record the lowest amount you can reasonably spend on each item. Total up all "reduced" amounts at the bottom of column 3, then subtract that amount from your total income. The resulting number is your maximum possible starting your *found debt reduction money*. Go through your credit card receipts and checkbook and add up all your monthly expenses. Use the list below. See where you can eliminate or reduce certain expenses.

MONTHLY EXPENSES	CURRENT	REDUCED
Retirement plan contributions		
Going out for lunch at work		
Dining out (other than work lunches)		
Groceries (use coupons)		
Telephone (including cell phone)		
Heating fuel		
Water/sewer		

Electricity		
Car cost (fuel and maintenance)		
Parking, tolls, etc. (car pool or bus)		
Car #1 payment		
Car #2 payment		
Insurance—automobile (higher deductibles)		
Insurance—health (higher deductibles)		
Insurance—home (umbrella insurance)		
Insurance—other		
Home equity loan payment		
Re-finance home mortgage (walk away)		
Other loan payment		
Child care		

Cable or satellite TV		
Movies out		
DVD rental		
Other entertainment		
Sports (golf, fishing, etc.)		
Health club		
Lawn maintenance		
Laundry and dry cleaning		
Pet food and care		
Subscriptions		
Online computer services		
Credit card payment		
Credit card payment		

Credit card payment		
Christmas gifts		
College education for children		
Private schools		
Emergency fund		
Other savings		
Total reduced monthly expenses =		

Total income—reduced monthly expenses _____
**(this is your *found debt reduction money* used to accelerate
your debt payments)**

5. **Other ideas to find extra money.**
   - Stop funding retirement until debt-free, except for matching contributions.
   - Get rid of your emergency fund. Once your credit card is paid, it becomes your emergency fund.
   - Evaluate/reduce holiday gift giving.
   - Check bank/credit card statement.
   - Stop smoking.
   - Properly maintain your home and car.
   - Never buy a brand-new car until debt-free.

- Never finance beyond 36 months.
- Take advantage of "cheap," meaningful vacations.
- Don't buy tools/boats you don't use a lot – rent them instead.
- Conserve utility usage.
- Avoid "Retail Therapy."
- Learn to say "No" to kids.
- Stop funding for children's education. Let them pay for their own college.
- All bonuses and pay raises go towards paying down debt.
- Eliminate private mortgage insurance (PMI) by paying down the mortgage balance to 80% of the home's original appraised value.
- Evaluate your real insurance needs.
- Auto insurance (get higher deductibles)
- Personal liability insurance
- Medical insurance
- Get higher deductibles.
- Get an umbrella attachment.
- Never buy extended warranties.
- Use coupons (retailmenot.com, gethoney.com).
- Stop getting tax refunds.
- Spare change jar
- Have only a cell phone.
- Minimize dining out, and make brown bag lunches.
- Simplify your lifestyle.
- Entertainment
- Movies
- Get rid of cable
- Shop at outlet malls/Goodwill/consignment shops
- See if you can refinance your home through Quicken Loans or a local bank.

The following ideas are for your office team members who want to get out of debt. You just need to learn how to be more efficient and be more profitable in your own practice.

An extra job becomes the rocket booster to accelerate your debt reduction. These recommendation are for your dental team members and spouses to pay off debt quicker. Endodontist should just focus on what they do best that is root canals and practice management.

- Make more at your job and put it toward debt.
- Do consulting work from home.
- Set up an eBay business at home.
- Visit clients at their home (bookkeepers or computer experts).
- Teach college at night.
- Check out the internet for "work-at-home jobs" (watch out for scams).
- Investigate doing multilevel marketing (Mary Kay) and watch out for scams.
- With an extra job, you could be debt-free three years faster.

6. Develop a spending journal and for a month: write down each purchase you make (except regularly scheduled bills). This includes incidentals such as coffee, parking and other items less than a dollar. Use mint.com or download from DoctorAce.com.

Date	Item purchased	Cash	Credit	Check	Amount

7. Use the snowball approach (described below) to pay off all debts within seven to ten years. Read through the snowball approach description, and then fill out the debt form to see how long it will take you to pay off all debts by making a 10% or 20% payment toward debt each month. I am not a big fan of budgeting. If you are serious about getting out of debt, automatically take 10% or 20% out of your bank account each month as if it were a tax. Live on the rest. Automation of the payments is the secret! Filling out the below form will help you understand your financial goals.

Snowball Worksheet

Identify your debts and record them on the Snowball Worksheet below (you can go to Doctorace.com and download the worksheet). First, pay all small debts (under $10,000) starting with the smallest. This "small debt" category includes credit card debt, consumer debt, auto loan balances, and small student loans. Start with the smallest debt (no matter how high or low the interest) and then use the money from your *debt reduction savings account* to pay it off first, while continuing to make the minimum payments on your other debts.

At the beginning, it's important to get momentum and see that you are making progress, so don't worry about the respective interest rates now. If the high credit card interest rate on a larger debt bothers you, you can always call the company and successfully negotiate a lower rate or transfer your balance to another credit card company with a lower rate.

Once you have paid off the first debt, you'll feel a sense of empowerment. Paying off that debt frees up additional money, which you add to your savings. Use this increased savings to pay down the next-smallest debt. Fill out the worksheet in pencil so that you can update it each month. This will help you keep on track and stay motivated.

As you pay down debt, you gain momentum and free up more money to pay off the next debt. The money that pays off these debts comes from increased income, reduced spending, and the extra money that becomes available as you pay off each debt. If you have money saved when you begin setting in motion *Dr. Ace's Financial Freedom Guide*, for the sake of your peace of mind, do *not* use that money for early debt reduction for at least six months. Below is an example of how we snowball paying off debt.

First, determine what percentage of income you want to pay toward debt. If you and your spouse's average income is $72,000, you would divide this by 12 months, giving you $6,000; after taxes that would be $5,000. Ten percentage of this would be $500 per month.

The $500 (10%) will be paid each month to the principal of the top loan in the chart. First, add the $500 to the Visa card $30 payment, giving you $530 per month to pay toward that loan, which will be paid off in two months. When the Visa card is paid off, apply that $530 plus $32 to the next MasterCard loan, which will result in $562; it will take three months to pay off *that* loan. Your efforts will continue to snowball throughout all your debt. The debts will be paid off in seven years and four months and you will have an extra $31,176 per year to invest, save, take vacations, send children through college, or work less.

$500 (10%) Paid Monthly to Principal of Top Loan in the Chart

Name of Debt	Total Balance (smallest to largest)	Monthly Payment	Accelerated Monthly Payment	Months to pay off
Visa Card	$1,000	$30	$530	2
MasterCard	$1,500	$32	$562	3
Department Store	$2,000	$36	$598	4
Car 1	$9,200	$520	$1,118	9
Car 2	$14,300	$750	$1,868	8
Home Equity Loan	$26,000	$370	$2,238	12

Mortgage at 4.5%	$155,000	$860	$3,098	50
Totals	$209,000	$2,598 ($31,176/yr.)		88 months (7yrs. 4mo.)

$1,000 (20%) Paid Monthly to Principal of Top Loan in the Chart

Name of Debt	Total Balance (smallest to largest)	Monthly Payment	Accelerated Monthly Payment	Months to pay off
Visa Card	$1,000	$30	$1,030	1
MasterCard	$1,500	$32	$1,062	2
Department Store	$2,000	$36	$1,098	2
Car 1	$9,200	$520	$1,618	6
Car 2	$14,300	$750	$2,368	6
Home Equity Loan	$26,000	$370	$2,738	10
Mortgage at 4.5%	$155,000	$860	$3,098	43
Totals	$209,000	$2,598 ($31,176/yr.)		70 months (5yrs. 7mo.)

Your Snowball Worksheet: Calculate Paying Off Your Debt (Annual household income: $ _____)

(Average American debt is 2.5 times the annual household income)

1. Determine your extra monthly payments: $_____

Try for 10% or more of your monthly take-home income. If you only have a home mortgage, then you should add 20% to 30% of your monthly take-home income to your mortgage payment.

2. Write down each debt in the first column below, prioritizing each debt from smallest to largest. Again, do not be overly concerned about the interest rate.

3. Using the snowball approach, add your accelerator margin to the smallest debt by making this new monthly payment. Put this in column 4. To determine when the debt will be paid off, divide this amount into the total balance of that debt by the new monthly payment in column 4, and put the number of months to pay off in column 5.

4. When this debt is paid off, add what used to be the monthly payment amount to the next smallest debt payment and place that in column 4. Again, divide this amount into the total balance of that debt by your new monthly payment in column 4. Put the number of months to pay off in column 5.

5. Continue adding each paid-off debt's monthly payment amount to its accelerated monthly payment and rolling the total amount to the next debt.

6. Add up the months in column 5 to determine when all debts will be paid off.

Name of Debt	Total Balance	Monthly Payment	Accelerated Monthly Payment	Months to Pay Off
1	2	3	4	5

Totals				

Things to keep in mind about your debt-elimination plan:
- Use only minimum payments to maximize the debt elimination process.
- Use only the principal and interest portion of your mortgage payment for purpose of calculation (not tax/insurance).
- Interest rates are not a big factor.
- Only non-recurring debts go into your debt-elimination plan.

7. Write and post your Financial Goals. For instance, "I am taking 10% of my income and paying off my debts. In six months (date), I will use 20% of my income toward an extra payment on my debts. I will pay off all credit card debts in one year (date), my car in two years (date), and my home in six years (date)." Then each month, review and challenge yourself to increase your debt reduction.

8. Develop a support group of either family or co-workers. In most families, issues of money cause the greatest stress and most do not understand how debt can keep a person in prison and take two-thirds of their income throughout their lifetime. In my office, I created and presented to them and their spouse a debt reduction plan which you will find at DoctorAce.com. In this program I showed them how to pay off debt, including their home, within ten years – thereby freeing up more money to invest in their retirement fund. I also showed them how to

invest safely with little risk and higher returns. (Remember Lisa's story in Chapter 2.)

9. Sign up for Dave Ramsey's financial peace University. Sometimes it helps go to a program where there is some accountability, and this is one of the better programs and is available everywhere. Http://www.daveramsey.com/fpu/

10. Continue to read books such as found in this book's references, and listen to audios about debt reduction, including the ones found at DoctoerAce.com.

11. Celebrate success.

This is NOT a *no-spending* plan; it is a *managed-spending* plan. I am not saying you shouldn't spend any money on the things you want, but I DO want you to be aware of the impact that each expenditure has on your ability to build your wealth. Most people can easily spend and live on half the amount they normally spend.

Appendix C

THE TEN PRINCIPLES OF INVESTMENT AND DEBT

By following these Ten Principles, you can achieve financial freedom:

1. The key to financial freedom is to make more than you spend or spend less than you make.
2. Make sure that every asset, large and small, adds meaning to your life.
3. Your best source of money is your ability to earn it, not investing.
4. If you have it made, don't risk it. You now can save enough money to retire early if you just play it smart by putting your money in safe investments as described in Chapter 5.
5. Because your source of money is your ability to earn it, rather than investment returns, focus on ways to increase your income: make yourself more valuable at your job, go back to school or work part-time until you become debt-free.
6. No matter how much you make, always automatically take 10% to 20% and pay off your debts. Spend less than you make or make more than you spend.
7. Only keep material possessions that add meaning to your life and get rid of the rest: it is just junk.
8. Create a safe and high yielding savings account in your own Personal Bank while protecting your family with a life insurance death benefit.

9. Purchasing a home is an effective use of debt. Although it is not a liquid asset, it adds meaning to your life. Homes have also proven to be good long-term investments and provide a hedge against inflation.

10. Always save for consumption; never borrow for consumer items, vacations, and so forth. Pay off all credit cards and consumer debt in full each month.

About the Author

Dr. Ace Goerig graduated from Case Western Reserve University Dental School in 1971 and was their distinguished alumnus in 2014. He then joined the US Army and retired as a colonel in 1991 after 20 years. He is a diplomat of the American Board of Endodontists and has been in private practice for 28 years in Olympia, Washington. Dr. Goerig has presented at every major national dental meeting and in 1996, co-founded Endo Mastery, a coaching program for endodontists.

In 2004, Dr. Goerig coauthored *Time and Money: Your Guide to Economic Freedom* with Kendrick Mercer to teach doctors and team members the secrets of becoming personally and financially free.

Dr. Ace has established two free websites to help dentists and their teams become financially free. They are DoctorAce.com and EndoMastery.com. He and his wife, Nancy, were married in 1969 and have five children and 13 grandchildren.